Contents

M000289222

© HMH Supplemental Publishers Inc.
© Houghton Mifflin Harcourt Publishing Company

Contents
Higher Scores on Reading and Language Arts, Grade 2

Introduction

This book is a tool to give children practice in taking standardized tests. Research shows that children who are acquainted with the scoring format of standardized tests score higher on those tests. The concepts presented in this book are typically found on standardized tests in Reading and Language Arts for this grade level. The goal of this book is to improve children's ability to perform well on standardized tests. Children will have multiple opportunities to practice answering items in multiple-choice format, as well as responding to open-ended items and writing prompts.

The tracking progress charts can help you pinpoint areas of weakness and strength with particular skills.

The book is divided into two main sections. The first section includes Test Tips and Practice for four main areas: Reading, Language Arts, Vocabulary, and Writing. Each Test Tips section provides a review of common skills and terms as well as strategies related to the topic. The Reading section focuses on literary texts (stories, poems, and drama) and informational texts (nonfiction and technical). The Language Arts section covers grammar, usage, and mechanics, as well as editing and revising skills. The Vocabulary section covers skills related to vocabulary acquisition, such as using context clues to determine the meaning of unfamiliar words and analyzing word relationships. The Writing section focuses on three types of writing prompts: opinion, informative, and narrative.

The second section provides children with Practice Tests for each area.

© HMH Supplemental Publishers Inc.
© Houghton Mifflin Harcourt Publishing Company

Tracking Progress Chart

Objective	Practice Item	Test Item	Mastery Yes	Mastery No	Comments
Literary Texts					
Understand and analyze plot. *(RL.2.4)	2, 7	9			
Understand and analyze characters and their actions.* (RL.2.3)	4, 18	8			
Understand and analyze setting.	9, 22	6			
Understand and analyze the theme, lesson, or moral of literary texts.* (RL.2.2)	5	10			
Understand and analyze point of view.	17	5, 13			
Understand and analyze elements of poetry.	16	17			
Understand and analyze literary devices.	19	15			
Make inferences from literary text.	8	7, 11			
Analyze and understand elements and structures of literary texts.* (RL.2.5)	21	1			
Identify the main idea of literary texts.	11	2, 18			
Identify specific details and events in a literary text.* (RL.2.1)	3, 10, 14	3, 14, 19			
Analyze how words and phrases supply rhythm and meaning in literary texts.* (RL.2.4)	15	20			
Understand how illustrations relate to the setting, plot, or characters of literary texts.* (RL.2.7)	12	4, 21			
Identify and understand figurative use of language in literary texts.	6, 20	16			
Summarize literary texts.	13	12			
Use context clues in words, sentences, and paragraphs to decode new vocabulary.* (RF.2.4c)	1				

* Aligns with Common Core State Standard

© HMH Supplemental Publishers Inc.
© Houghton Mifflin Harcourt Publishing Company

Tracking Progress Chart
Higher Scores on Reading and Language Arts, Grade 2

Objective	Practice Item	Test Item	Mastery Yes	Mastery No	Comments
Informational Texts					
Identify the main idea of a text and the details that support it.* (RI.2.2)	4, 13, 18, 21	22, 29, 42, 45			
Analyze an author's purpose.* (RI.2.6)	1, 16, 24	23, 33			
Analyze how text structures of informational texts contribute to the development of ideas.* (RI.2.3)	2, 7, 20	37, 46			
Make inferences from an informational text.	5, 9, 15, 17, 25	27, 47			
Use text features to locate key facts or information.* (RI.2.5)	22, 28	30, 36, 48			
Summarize informational texts.	12, 27	35			
Identify specific details, facts, or events in a text.* (RI.2.1)	6, 11, 14	24, 28, 32, 34, 39, 41, 43			
Analyze how media and graphics contribute to a topic or issue.* (RI.2.7)	10, 19	31, 44			
Identify and understand technical or specialized language in informational texts.* (RI.2.4)	3, 23	25, 38, 40			
Evaluate how arguments and claims are supported by evidence and reasons.* (RI.2.8)	8, 26	26			

© HMH Supplemental Publishers Inc.
© Houghton Mifflin Harcourt Publishing Company

Objective	Practice Item	Test Item	Mastery Yes	Mastery No	Comments
Language Conventions					
Demonstrate control of grammar, usage, and sentence structure.* (L.2.1)	9, 14	6, 13, 14			
Vary sentence patterns (simple and compound) for meaning, interest, and style.* (L.2.1f)	2, 12	1, 10			
Understand agreement.	1, 17, 18	4			
Use adjectives and adverbs correctly.* (L.2.1e)	4, 15, 16	7			
Form past tense of regular and irregular verbs correctly.* (L.2.1d)	5, 10	9, 12			
Use pronouns correctly.* (L.2.1c)	6, 19	3, 11			
Use case forms of personal pronouns correctly.* (L.2.1c)	3, 13	5			
Demonstrate control of standard English conventions and mechanics.* (L.2.2)	32, 33, 36, 38	19, 23, 29			
Use capitalization correctly, including holidays, product names, and geographic names.* (L.2.2a)	22, 24, 37	15, 27			
Use punctuation correctly.	20, 27, 31	17, 21			
Use commas correctly, including in conventional uses (greetings and closing of letters).* (L.2.2b)	23, 25, 26	16, 24			
Use apostrophes correctly.* (L.2.2c)	21, 28, 34	20, 25, 26			
Use irregular, plural nouns correctly.* (L.2.1b)	7, 11	2			
Use collective nouns correctly.* (L.2.1a)	8	8			
Use correct spelling.* (L.2.2d)	29, 30, 35	18, 22, 28			
Writing					
Write opinion essays.* (W.2.1)	Prompt 1	Prompt 1			
Write informative essays.* (W.2.2)	Prompt 2	Prompt 2			
Write narrative essays.* (W.2.3)	Prompt 3	Prompt 3			

© HMH Supplemental Publishers Inc.
© Houghton Mifflin Harcourt Publishing Company

Tracking Progress Chart
Higher Scores on Reading and Language Arts, Grade 2

Objective	Practice Item	Test Item	Mastery Yes	Mastery No	Comments
Vocabulary					
Identify antonyms.	4, 10	30			
Identify synonyms.	3, 15	37			
Use context clues in words, sentences, and paragraphs to decode new vocabulary.* (L.2.4a)	6, 14	32			
Identify and understand connotative and figurative use of language.	12	40			
Identify and use correctly multiple-meaning words.* (L.2.4)	1, 16	31			
Categorize words based on real-life connections between words and their use.* (L.2.5a)	11				
Identify and use suffixes, prefixes, and roots to understand and create words.* (L.2.b, L.2.c)	8, 17	33, 35			
Understand word relationships.* (L.2.5)	13	38			
Distinguish shades of meaning among closely related words, such as verbs and adjectives.* (L.2.5b)	5	39			
Use meanings of individual words to understand the meaning of compound words.* (L.2.4d)	2, 7	34			
Understand how to use dictionary entries to determine pronunciation and clarify meaning.* (L.2.4e)	9, 18	36			

© HMH Supplemental Publishers Inc.
© Houghton Mifflin Harcourt Publishing Company

Reading Test Tips and Practice

Taking Reading Tests

In the Reading Test Tips and Practice section, you will read some tips for answering multiple-choice questions and open-ended questions. Next, you will review common skills and terms and learn about strategies for answering different kinds of questions. Then, you will be asked to read stories and passages and answer questions.

Answering Multiple-Choice Questions

Here are some tips for taking any reading test:

- First, **read the passage**. Read it as if you were not taking a test. Read it again if you do not understand it at first.
- Next, **look at the big picture**. To do this, ask yourself:
  - What is the title?

  - What is the story or passage mostly about?

  - Why did the author write it? to inform? to entertain? to show how to do something?

- Then, **read the questions**. This will help you know what information to look for when you read it again.
- Read the story or passage again. **Underline information** that helps you answer the questions.
- **Go back to the questions.** Try to answer each one in your mind before looking at the answer choices.
- Last, **read *all* the answer choices. Get rid of those that are not correct.** After this, mark the best answer. Remember, one answer is best. Some answer choices are not true. Some are about the wrong part of the story. Some include too much information. Some include too little information.

Answering Open-Ended Questions

Reading tests often include open-ended, or short-answer, questions. These questions do not have answer choices. They ask you to write your answer.

Here are some tips for answering open-ended questions:
- Read the whole story or passage. Pay close attention to the most important events and characters.
- Read each question carefully. If you cannot answer the question at first, skip it and come back to it later.
- Return to the story or passage. Look for details or examples you need to write your answer.

Test Tips for Reading Literature

Using Context Clues

One way to figure out the meaning of a word is to use **context clues**. These are words and sentences around the word. Use the following steps to answer questions about words you do not know:

Step 1: Read the sentence that contains the unknown word. See if the words before or after it give clues to the word's meaning. Then read sentences around the word and look for clues.

Step 2: Use the clues to guess the word's meaning.

Step 3: Check your answer by using it in the sentence in place of the unknown word.

Summarizing

Follow these steps to choose the best answer to a **summary** question:

Step 1: Read the story or passage slowly and carefully. For stories, look for the main characters and only the most important events. For nonfiction passages, look for important ideas and details.

Step 2: Think about each answer choice. Get rid of those that tell a single detail. Get rid of the ones that have little or nothing to do with the story or passage. Look for the most important details.

Step 3: Be sure that you choose the answer that tells about the whole passage. For stories, make sure it tells about the main characters and most important events. For nonfiction, make sure it tells about the important ideas and details.

Inferences

An **inference** is an educated guess based on what you read and what you already know. Put the author's ideas and your ideas together to make an inference. Use the following steps to answer inference questions:

Step 1: Read the story or passage one time. Then carefully read it again.

Step 2: Find key words in the answer choices that match words in the story or passage.

Step 3: Think about what the author said and what you know. This will help you find the correct answer.

Name _____ Date _____

Understanding Main Ideas and Supporting Details

The most important point in a paragraph or story is the **main idea**.
Follow these steps to identify a main idea:

Step 1: Read the story or passage and identify the topic.

Step 2: Look at the details. How are the details all alike? The details
should all tell about the main idea. **Hint:** For nonfiction,
pay attention to the first and last sentences. You may find a
sentence that tells the main idea. For stories, pay attention to
the conflict and what characters learn during the story.

Step 3: Say the main idea in your own words. Then, look for an
answer that closely matches your own. Be careful not to
choose an answer that tells just one detail.

Step 4: Check to make sure that the details all tell about the main idea
you chose.

Analyzing Character

A **character** is a person or animal in a story or poem. An author tells
about a character in six different ways:

- by describing how the character looks and dresses
- by letting the reader hear the character speak
- by showing the reader how the character acts
- by letting the reader know the character's thoughts and feelings
- by showing what other characters think or say about the character
- by telling the reader what the character is like (such as kind, mean,
  or brave)

Identifying Setting

Setting is the place where a story or poem takes place. The setting can also tell when the story or poem takes place. Look for clues that answer the questions *Where did this happen? When did this happen?*

Analyzing Plot

Plot is the order of events that makes up a story. The plot tells what happens.

- Look for time-order words like *first, next, then, finally* to help you tell the order of events.
- Sometimes a story begins by telling who the characters are and what their problem is. Then the story events tell how the problem is solved.

Identifying Point of View

Point of view is who is telling a story. Point of view can be first person or third person.

- First-person point of view: One of the characters, using the pronoun *I*, tells the story.
- Third-person point of view: A narrator tells about the characters and events.

Analyzing Theme

The **theme** of a story is the main idea or lesson that the author is trying to teach. A writer may or may not directly state the theme. Use these steps to identify a story's theme:

Step 1: Think about the main problem of the story and how the characters act.

Step 2: Ask yourself if the characters learned any lessons.

Step 3: Choose the answer that best tells the lesson the characters learned.

Analyzing Elements of Poetry

Rhyme – words that have the same ending sound

    Example: *box* and *fox*, *bright* and *light*

Rhythm – repeating sounds or beats in phrases or sentences

Identifying Literary Devices

Authors use different literary devices to help readers form pictures in their minds. Test questions may ask you to find literary devices or to tell what they mean.

Alliteration – repeating the same beginning consonant sounds in words that are close together

    Example: Sally sells seashells by the seashore. (repeating *s* sound)

Figurative language – describing one thing by comparing it to a different thing

    Example: I was so hungry that I ate like a horse.

Imagery – words and phrases that describe something using sight, touch, smell, sound, or taste

    Example: The red and yellow leaves fall to the ground. (sight) They crunch under my feet. (sound) I pick one up and it crumbles in my hand. (touch)

Read the story. Then answer the questions. For multiple-choice items, darken the circle by the correct answer. For the open-ended item, write the answer.

A Little Pool Water

Juan held his goggles in one hand and his towel in the other. Today was his first day of swim practice. He really didn't know how to swim very well. He wasn't even sure if he wanted to be on the swim team. But a bunch of his friends were on the team. They had talked him into joining. So now he had to swim—a lot.

The coach blew his whistle. "Everybody in! Let's see you swim!" he yelled.

For an hour, Juan swam back and forth with the rest of the team. He always came in last.

"How was practice?" his mom asked when she came to pick him up.

"I think I drank the whole pool!" Juan replied.

"Don't worry," said Juan's mother. She gave him a big hug. "It will get easier."

Day after day, Juan went to swim practice. Day after day, he drank a *lot* of pool water.

"Juan," said his coach one day. "I want you to swim in this Saturday's swim meet."

"Okay," said Juan. "I'll do my best."

8

When Saturday came, Juan tried hard. He got a green ribbon. "Everyone who swims gets one," he told his mother. "Even if you're slow, like me," he said sadly.

"That's okay," said his mom. "You swam your best. That is what's important. You'll get faster if you keep practicing."

All summer Juan went to swim practice. All summer he gulped down pool water.

Finally, it was time for the last meet of the season. Juan's family came to watch him. By the end of the swim meet, Juan had a third-place medal. He held it up and grinned from ear to ear.

"You're lucky!" said his sister Rosa.

"It wasn't luck," said Juan. "I worked hard." He looked at his shiny new medal. "And I drank a little pool water!"

1. Read these sentences from the story.

> He wasn't even sure if he wanted to be on the swim team. But a <u>bunch</u> of his friends were on the team. They had talked him into joining.

What does <u>bunch</u> mean?

Ⓐ swimmer

Ⓑ best friends

Ⓒ a lot

Ⓓ teammates

2. What happened in the middle of the story?

Ⓐ Juan worried that he could not swim well.

Ⓑ Juan won a green ribbon at the meet.

Ⓒ Juan got scared that his friends would laugh at him.

Ⓓ Rosa told Juan that he was lucky.

3. Why did Juan tell Rosa that he wasn't lucky to win the medal?

Ⓐ He wanted to win first place.

Ⓑ He did not make Rosa proud.

Ⓒ He didn't want to be on the swim team.

Ⓓ He earned the medal with hard work.

4. How does Juan feel about joining the swim team?

Ⓐ unsure

Ⓑ excited

Ⓒ scared

Ⓓ pleased

5. What lesson does the story teach?

Ⓐ Practice helps you do better.

Ⓑ The slowest person can win a race.

Ⓒ Friends help one another.

Ⓓ Only do things you're good at.

6. Read this sentence from the story.

> He held it up and
> <u>grinned from ear to ear.</u>

What does <u>grinned from ear to ear</u> mean in this sentence?

Ⓐ Juan was not really happy.

Ⓑ Juan's smile was very big.

Ⓒ Juan wiggled his ears when he smiled.

Ⓓ Juan looked from one ear to the other.

7. Complete the chart with an event from the story.

Beginning
Juan joined the swimming team.

Middle
Juan practiced all summer.

End

_____

Read the story. Then answer the questions. For multiple-choice items, darken the circle by the correct answer. For the open-ended item, write the answer.

How Does the Lighthouse Help Sailors?

Emily and her mother went to the beach in Cape May, New Jersey, last summer. One day they went to see the lighthouse.

Emily and her mom climbed to the top of the tower. From there, they could see very far. They saw miles of ocean and beach. It was a beautiful sight.

Mr. Beal, the man who works at the lighthouse, told Emily and her mom all about it. The Cape May Lighthouse is 131 years old. It is all white, and it is 165 feet tall. It has a very strong light. Mr. Beal said that the lighthouse is still very important to sailors. Sailors can see its light from 24 miles out at sea. The light helps ships come into Delaware Bay.

Mr. Beal told Emily and her mom how the sailors take care of the lighthouse. Their jobs are cleaning the light and making sure it is working. Mr. Beal said that many people who live in Cape May also help keep the lighthouse in good shape. They want others to enjoy it for many years to come. Some people help fix parts of the lighthouse. Some clean the lighthouse. Others paint it.

Emily can't wait to visit the lighthouse again next summer. She wants Mr. Beal to show the lighthouse to her best friend, Jill.

8. Why are lighthouses close to the ocean?

   Ⓐ They are beautiful for people to look at.

   Ⓑ They let people see the ocean waves.

   Ⓒ They give people a place to visit at the beach.

   Ⓓ They help sailors coming in on ships.

9. What did Emily and her mother see from the top of the lighthouse?

   Ⓐ the man who works at the lighthouse

   Ⓑ people who live in Cape May

   Ⓒ miles of ocean and beach

   Ⓓ a very strong light

10. Why is the lighthouse important?

   Ⓐ It gives Mr. Beal a job.

   Ⓑ It keeps visitors safe.

   Ⓒ It helps sailors at sea find land.

   Ⓓ It lets sailors see for miles from the tower.

11. Which of these is another good name for this story?

   Ⓐ "Emily and Her Mom Have Fun at the Beach"

   Ⓑ "A Visit to a Lighthouse"

   Ⓒ "Sailing in Delaware Bay"

   Ⓓ "How to Take Care of a Lighthouse"

12. Look at the picture on page 12. Where does this story take place?

   Ⓐ in a ship

   Ⓑ in a house

   Ⓒ on a rock

   Ⓓ at a lighthouse

13. What is the **best** summary of the story?

Ⓐ Emily and her mother climbed to the top of the lighthouse. Mr. Beal told them all about the lighthouse's history. Emily wants to visit the lighthouse next summer.

Ⓒ Mr. Beal and Emily climbed to the top of a tower. They saw ocean, beach, and a lighthouse. Sailors saw the lighthouse's light and came in safely.

Ⓑ Sailors took care of a lighthouse. They painted it and cleaned the light. Sailors will come back next summer to visit the lighthouse again.

Ⓓ Mr. Beal told Emily all about the Cape May Lighthouse. He brought sailors to see the lighthouse. Then, Emily and her mom climbed the tower.

---

14. Using the story, write one detail to complete the web.

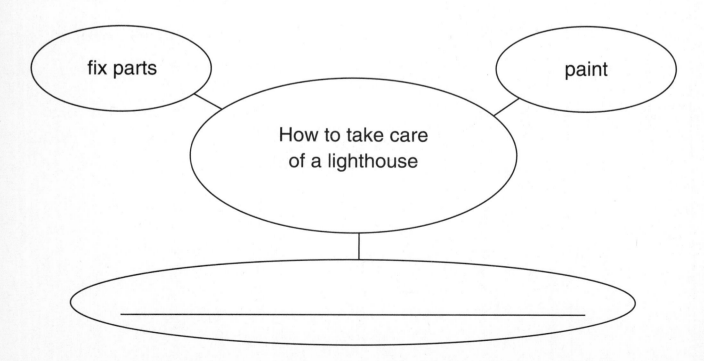

Name _____ Date _____

Read the poem. Then answer the questions. For multiple-choice items, darken the circle by the correct answer. For the open-ended item, write the answer.

A New School

Today was my first day
At the new school in my new town.
Mom said, "Emily, please put on a smile!"
But all I could do was frown.

I took a seat on the bus alone,
My knapsack by my side.
Would I make any friends at this new school?
I wondered and I sighed.

At the next bus stop,
A girl sat down next to me.
I found out she's in my second-grade class.
And her name is also Emily!

When the bus dropped us off at school,
I met Emily's friends Cara, James, and Brad.
Why was I so worried?
A new school isn't all that bad.

15. Which two words from "A New School" rhyme?

(A) first/day

(B) new/town

(C) day/smile

(D) town/frown

16. "A New School" is a poem because

(A) it tells a story.

(B) it has rhythm and rhyme.

(C) it has exclamations and questions.

(D) it is about make-believe people.

17. "A New School" is being told by

(A) Mom.

(B) Emily.

(C) Cara.

(D) Brad.

18. In "A New School," how did Emily's feelings change?

(A) She decided her new school wasn't all that bad.

(B) She became more worried about school.

(C) She grew more tired from the bus ride.

(D) She felt her old school was better than her new one.

Read the poem. Then answer the questions. For multiple-choice items, darken the circle by the correct answer. For the open-ended item, write the answer.

Winter Trees

The line of trees
Sways in the winter wind
Like white birds
Flying from fence posts.

With each gust of wind
Icy branches talk softly,
Chatter in the frozen field.

The wind humming through
the trees
is the sound of birds
lifting from rest.

19. What does the writer compare the trees to in "Winter Trees"?

Ⓐ fence posts

Ⓑ frozen fields

Ⓒ birds

Ⓓ branches

20. In "Winter Trees," why did the icy branches "chatter in the frozen field"?

Ⓐ The ice was melting.

Ⓑ The branches were like teeth that chatter when a person is very cold.

Ⓒ The trees were close together and looked like they were talking to one another.

Ⓓ When the wind blew through the branches, they made a chattering noise.

21. Read the lines from "Winter Trees."

> The wind humming through the trees
> is the sound of birds
> lifting from rest.

Trees are compared to birds to show how

Ⓐ the trees look like the shape of birds.

Ⓑ the wind sounds like flapping bird wings.

Ⓒ the trees are the color of flying birds.

Ⓓ the trees feel as soft as a bird's feathers.

22. What is the setting of "Winter Trees"?

_____

_____

Test Tips for Reading Informational Texts

Identifying the Main Idea and Supporting Details

The most important point in a reading passage is the main idea. The main idea must be about the entire passage, not just a part of it. Follow these steps in order to identify a passage's main idea:

Step 1:   Read the passage and determine the topic. The title and headings are clues to the passage topic.

Step 2:   Look at what all the details have in common. The details should point to the main idea. **Hint:** Pay attention to the first and last sentences. You may find a sentence that states the main idea.

Step 3:   State the main idea in your own words. Then, look for an answer that closely matches your own. Be careful not to choose a detail that tells about the main idea as your answer.

Step 4:   Check to make sure that the details in the passage are all about the main idea in your answer.

Identifying Author's Purpose

There are four general purposes authors have for writing. Use the steps below for help in answering questions about purpose:

Step 1:   Look in the text for clues such as the ones below.

- pictures, diagrams, maps, charts, headings, and numbered items (**to inform**)

- words like *should* and *must*, or *worst* and *best* (**to persuade**)

- use of the word *I* and words about feelings (**to express**)

- use of make-believe, dialogue, rhymes, adventure, or humor (**to entertain**)

Step 2:   Look for the choice that most closely matches the clues.

Analyzing Text Structure

Understanding the way a text is organized can help readers follow the writer's ideas. Four kinds of organization are listed below.

- **Cause and effect** shows how one event leads to, or causes, another event. Some of the clue words and phrases that signal cause and effect are *because*, *since*, and *so that*.

- **Time order** shows events in the order in which they happen. Look for time order words, such as *first*, *next*, *then*, and *finally*.

- **Compare and contrast** tells how things are alike and different. Some clue words that tell how things are different are *but*, *either*, *or*, *different*, and *yet*. Some clue words that tell how things are alike are *also*, *alike*, *as well*, *both*, and *too*.

- **Problem and solution** presents a problem and then tells a solution for the problem.

Use the steps below to help analyze text structure:

Step 1: Look for clue words that tell about a kind of organization.

Step 2: Look for important ideas. See whether these ideas are connected.

Step 3: Look for the answer choice that best matches the organization.

Using Text Features

Headings, captions, labels, maps, charts, tables, diagrams, and pictures are all text features. Text features such as headings, captions, and labels help readers find information. Text features such as maps, charts, tables, diagrams, and pictures present information. When you see text features, use the steps below:

Step 1:   Read the title, labels, and legend before you try to figure out the information.

Step 2:   Read numbers carefully.

Step 3:   Looks for clues found in the feature.

Using Context Clues

One way to tell the meaning of an unfamiliar word is to use context clues. Often a word's meaning is found in the words and sentences around it. Use the following steps to answer questions about words you do not know:

Step 1:   See if the words and sentences around the unfamiliar word give clues to the word's meaning.

Step 2:   Use the context clues to guess the unfamiliar word's meaning.

Step 3:   Check your definition by using it in place of the unfamiliar word in the sentence. Ask yourself, does the definition make sense in the sentence?

Summarizing a Text

Follow these steps to choose the best answer to a summary question:

Step 1: Look for the main idea and the most important supporting details as you read the passage slowly and carefully.

Step 2: Think about each answer choice. Get rid of those that tell a single detail from the passage. Get rid of those that tell a general statement about the passage but tell no important details. Get rid of those that have little or nothing to do with the passage.

Step 3: Be sure that the answer you choose is about the <u>whole</u> passage. Make sure it includes the main idea and only the important supporting details.

Making Inferences

An author may tell something about an idea. You must also think about what you know about the idea. Put the author's ideas and your ideas together to make an inference. Use the following steps to answer inference questions:

Step 1: Read the passage one time. Then carefully read it again.

Step 2: Find key words in the answer choices that match words in the passage.

Step 3: Think about what the author said and what you know. This will help you find the correct answer.

Name _____ Date _____

Informational Text

Read the passage. Then answer the questions. For multiple-choice items, darken the circle by the correct answer. For the open-ended item, write the answer.

Grandma Moses

Imagine never taking an art lesson but becoming a famous painter. That's what happened to a tiny grandmother with gray hair. Her name was Anna Mary Robertson Moses. People called her Grandma Moses.

On September 7, 1860, Anna Mary Robertson was born in the state of New York. She added "Moses" to her name when she got married. She and her husband lived in the state of Virginia. They raised their children on a farm. After her husband died in 1927, Moses moved back to New York.

Grandma Moses liked to make pictures. First, Grandma Moses loved to sew pictures on cloth. Then, as she got older, her hands began to hurt when she sewed. So Grandma Moses decided to paint pictures instead.

She painted her first picture on a piece of canvas. She used house paint! At first she copied pictures from postcards. Then she began to paint things she remembered from her childhood.

When Grandma Moses was a young girl, she saw people using the sap from maple trees to make syrup and sugar. "Sugaring off" is a special name for what happens when sap is collected from sugar maple trees and made into maple sugar and syrup.

Grandma Moses painted many pictures about sugaring off. She showed people carrying buckets of sap from maple trees. To make the light on the snow dance and sparkle, Grandma Moses added touches of glitter to her paintings.

Grandma Moses started painting when she was 75 years old. She painted over 1,600 paintings. In fact, she painted 25 pictures in the last year of her life, when she was 100 years old!

1. Why did the author write "Grandma Moses"?

   Ⓐ to give directions for painting

   Ⓑ to share a funny story about Grandma Moses

   Ⓒ to tell about Grandma Moses' life and art

   Ⓓ to explain what sugaring off is

2. How did the author write the events in the life of Grandma Moses?

   Ⓐ as problem and solution

   Ⓑ by cause and effect

   Ⓒ in the order they happened

   Ⓓ by telling how they are alike and different

3. Read this sentence from the passage.

> When Grandma Moses was a young girl, she saw people using the <u>sap</u> from maple trees to make syrup and sugar.

What does the word <u>sap</u> mean?

Ⓐ liquid inside a tree

Ⓑ leaves on a tree

Ⓒ insects from a tree

Ⓓ birds in a tree

4. Read this paragraph from the passage.

> Grandma Moses liked to make pictures. First, Grandma Moses loved to sew pictures on cloth. Then, as she got older, her hands began to hurt when she sewed. So Grandma Moses decided to paint pictures instead.

Which question is answered in the paragraph?

Ⓐ What kinds of pictures did Grandma Moses paint?

Ⓑ When did Grandma Moses start sewing pictures?

Ⓒ What made Grandma Moses stop painting?

Ⓓ Why did Grandma Moses start painting?

5. What made Grandma Moses different from many other famous painters?

   Ⓐ She painted very fast.

   Ⓑ She never took art lessons.

   Ⓒ She painted pictures of winter.

   Ⓓ She painted pictures of nature.

6. Grandma Moses made snow in her paintings look special by

   Ⓐ using house paint.

   Ⓑ using glitter.

   Ⓒ sewing on the canvas.

   Ⓓ painting on canvas.

7. Number the events in Grandma Moses' life in the order they happened.

_____ Grandma Moses started painting pictures on canvas.

_____ Grandma Moses painted pictures about sugaring off.

_____ Grandma Moses sewed pictures on cloth.

_____ Grandma Moses turned 100 years old.

Read the passage. Then answer the questions. For multiple-choice items, darken the circle by the correct answer. For the open-ended item, write the answer.

Buttercups

Buttercups are bright yellow flowers that grow along country roadsides and fields from May until September. They make a ride through the country more beautiful.

People used to think that if cows ate buttercups, the butter made from the cows' milk would be a brighter yellow. But this is not so. Farmers say that buttercups are weeds and are too bitter for cows to eat.

The buttercup usually has five smooth, shiny flower parts that look like petals. Children sometimes like to hold buttercups under each other's chin. If a bright yellow spot appears under the chin, it is said that the child likes to eat butter.

© HMH Supplemental Publishers Inc.
© Houghton Mifflin Harcourt Publishing Company

8. Which sentence from the passage tells how the author feels about buttercups?

Ⓐ They make a ride through the country more beautiful.

Ⓑ Farmers say that buttercups are weeds and are too bitter for cows to eat.

Ⓒ The buttercup usually has five smooth, shiny flower parts that look like petals.

Ⓓ If a bright yellow spot appears under the chin, it is said that the child likes to eat butter.

9. What clue in the passage tells that buttercups grow in the summer?

Ⓐ bright yellow flowers

Ⓑ grow along country roadsides

Ⓒ from May until September

Ⓓ if cows ate buttercups

10. How does the picture help you know where to go to find buttercups?

Ⓐ It shows a road in a rural area.

Ⓑ It shows flowers from a flower shop.

Ⓒ It shows a fence made of wood.

Ⓓ It shows a field in the country.

11. How do children tell if their friends like butter?

Ⓐ They check the color of a cow's milk.

Ⓑ They hold buttercups under each other's chin.

Ⓒ They feed buttercups to cows.

Ⓓ They pick the buttercups in the fields.

12. Which sentences are a good summary of "Buttercups"?

Ⓐ Buttercups are yellow flowers that grow in fields. Cows do not eat the bitter weeds. Some children hold them under friends' chins to see if they like butter.

Ⓑ Buttercups are used to tell what color a cow's milk will be. They are bitter flowers. Buttercups are used to make butter.

Ⓒ Buttercups grow in the summer. They are planted by farmers. Children hold them under cows to see if a cow will make yellow butter.

Ⓓ Buttercups have five smooth petals. They grow in fields. They grow along country roads. If a cow eats them, its milk is a bright yellow.

13. What is the main idea of the second paragraph?

Ⓐ Buttercups are bitter weeds.

Ⓑ Buttercups do not change the color of butter made from a cow's milk.

Ⓒ Cows eat buttercups and then are milked.

Ⓓ People used to have strange ideas about butter.

14. Why might a friend hold a buttercup under your chin?

_____

_____

Name _____ Date _____

Read the passage. Then answer the questions. For multiple-choice items, darken the circle by the correct answer. For the open-ended item, write the answer.

How to Make a Pinecone Bird Feeder

For a fun craft project on a winter's day, try making a pinecone bird feeder. With an adult's help, you can make this special treat that birds around your neighborhood will enjoy.

Materials

- string
- scissors
- birdseed
- plate
- peanut butter
- pinecone
- butter knife

Directions

First, cut a long piece of string. Tie the string to the top of the pinecone. Next, use the butter knife to spread peanut butter on the pinecone. Be sure to completely cover the pinecone with peanut butter. Pour birdseed onto the plate. Roll the pinecone around in the birdseed. After it is coated with birdseed, your pinecone feeder is done!

© HMH Supplemental Publishers Inc.
© Houghton Mifflin Harcourt Publishing Company

15. What is used to hang the pinecone bird feeder from the tree?

   Ⓐ pinecone

   Ⓑ string

   Ⓒ peanut butter

   Ⓓ birdseed

16. Why did the author write this passage?

   Ⓐ to give information about different kinds of birds

   Ⓑ to get readers to like birds

   Ⓒ to show how to make a pinecone bird feeder

   Ⓓ to tell why birds like pinecones

17. Why is peanut butter used to make the bird feeder?

   Ⓐ The birdseed sticks to the peanut butter.

   Ⓑ The string sticks to the peanut butter.

   Ⓒ Birds will eat only peanut butter.

   Ⓓ The peanut butter keeps the pinecone warm.

18. What happens right after birdseed is poured onto the plate?

   Ⓐ The plate is cut with the scissors.

   Ⓑ The pinecone is rolled in the birdseed.

   Ⓒ The peanut butter is spread on the plate.

   Ⓓ The bird feeder is hung on a tree.

19. What picture could be added to help the reader better understand the passage?

    Ⓐ a pine tree covered in pinecones

    Ⓑ a store that sells birdseed

    Ⓒ birds looking for food in the winter

    Ⓓ a pinecone being rolled in birdseed

20. What is found in the Directions section of the passage?

    Ⓐ when to make the bird feeder

    Ⓑ what you need to make the bird feeder

    Ⓒ the steps to follow to make the bird feeder

    Ⓓ who should help you make the bird feeder

21. Write the step that completes the chart.

| **1** |
| Cut string and tie it to the pinecone. |

| **2** |
| _____ |
| _____ |

| **3** |
| Pour birdseed onto plate. |

| **4** |
| Roll pinecone in birdseed. |

© HMH Supplemental Publishers Inc.
© Houghton Mifflin Harcourt Publishing Company

Name _____ Date _____

Read the recipe. Then answer the questions. For multiple-choice items, darken the circle by the correct answer. For the open-ended item, write the answer.

Peanut Butter Balls

(serves 8)

You will need:

½ cup unsweetened peanut butter

2 ½ tablespoons nonfat dry milk

2 tablespoons raisins

¼ cup unsweetened coconut

sesame seeds (optional)

Follow these steps:

Mix all the ingredients, except the sesame seeds. Form the mixture into balls. Roll the balls in the sesame seeds. Eat and enjoy! If you like, roll the balls in chocolate sprinkles instead of the sesame seeds. Or, you can use any other topping you like.

22. Where in the passage can you find how many servings the recipe makes?

   Ⓐ "Follow these steps" section

   Ⓑ "You will need" section

   Ⓒ under the title

   Ⓓ at the end of the recipe

23. In this recipe, the word <u>optional</u> means

   Ⓐ something you must use.

   Ⓑ something you should add.

   Ⓒ something you may or may not do.

   Ⓓ something you must wash first.

24. Why did the author write this passage?

   Ⓐ to give an opinion about cooking

   Ⓑ to get the reader to like coconut

   Ⓒ to entertain with a funny story

   Ⓓ to tell how to make a snack

25. About how long would it most likely take to make this recipe?

   Ⓐ one hour

   Ⓑ fifteen minutes

   Ⓒ two hours

   Ⓓ forty-five minutes

© HMH Supplemental Publishers Inc.
© Houghton Mifflin Harcourt Publishing Company

26. Which sentence from the passage tells you the author likes peanut butter balls?

Ⓐ Form the mixture into balls.

Ⓑ Eat and enjoy!

Ⓒ If you like, roll the balls in chocolate sprinkles instead of the sesame seeds.

Ⓓ Or, you can use any other topping you like.

27. What is the **best** summary of the passage?

Ⓐ Mix peanut butter, nonfat dry milk, raisins, and coconut together. Form into balls. Roll the balls in sesame seeds.

Ⓑ You can roll the balls in sprinkles or in sesame seeds. You can use other toppings too.

Ⓒ Roll balls in sesame seeds. Then mix peanut butter and raisins together. Finally, roll in chocolate sprinkles.

Ⓓ Cooking does not have to be hard. It is easy to make peanut butter balls. This recipe makes 8 balls.

28. Which section tells what you should gather together <u>before</u> you start mixing?

_____

Language Arts and Vocabulary
Test Tips and Practice

Taking Language Arts Tests

In the Language Arts Tips and Practice section, you will review common skills and terms about grammar, usage, and mechanics. Then, you will read passages that have errors and answer questions about how to fix the errors. You will also answer stand-alone questions.

Test Tips for Grammar and Usage

Nouns and Pronouns

A noun is a word used to name a person, place, thing, or idea.
Paula went to the **library.** She got three **books** about **butterflies.**

A pronoun is a word used in place of one or more nouns or pronouns.
I like to read books. **I** like to read fairy tales with **my** sisters. **They** like **them** too.

Verbs

A verb is a word that shows action.
Terry **swam** across the lake. Then, he **rested.** He **stretched** on the grass.

Noun and Verb Agreement

When a noun names only one, use an action verb with *s*.
Margaret loves raisins.
The **bear sleeps** in a cave.
My **brother plays** the flute.

When a noun names only one, use the helping verb *is*.
Margaret is eating raisins.
The **bear is sleeping** in a cave.
My **brother is playing** the flute.

© HMH Supplemental Publishers Inc.
© Houghton Mifflin Harcourt Publishing Company

When a noun names more than one, the action verb does not have an *s*.

The **twins make** popcorn.

The three **puppies sit** in the window.

The **children walk** in the hall.

When a noun names more than one, use the helping verb *are*.

The **twins are making** popcorn.

The three **puppies are sitting** in the window.

The **children are walking** in the hall.

Adjectives and Adverbs

An adjective is a word used to describe a noun or a pronoun. Adjectives tell *what kind*, *which one*, *how much*, or *how many*.

Buster is a **funny** dog. He has **one brown** ear and **one white** ear.

An adverb is a word that tells about a verb. Adverbs tell *where*, *when*, *how*, or *to what extent*. Many adverbs end in *-ly*.

Buster ran **quickly across** the room. He barked **before** he got to the door. Then he **suddenly** sat up as if nothing happened.

Personal Pronouns

A pronoun refers to a noun or another pronoun. If a noun tells about only one, use the pronouns *he*, *him*, *she*, *her*, and *it*. If a noun tells about more than one, use the pronouns *we*, *us*, *they*, and *them*. If telling about yourself, use *I* and *me*.

I was playing with Mia. **I** hit a vase. **It** fell on the floor. Mia helped **me** clean **it** up. **She** is a good friend. After that, **we** went outside to play.

Test Tips for Mechanics

Capitalization

Capitalize the first word in every sentence.
The kite is in the tree.

Capitalize the pronoun *I*.
Mom said that I can watch one TV show.

Capitalize proper nouns.
A proper noun names a certain person, place, or thing.
I went shopping with Mrs. Kitt in Springfield.

Capitalize names of holidays.
My aunt and uncle came to visit on Thanksgiving.

Punctuation

End marks

Use a period at the end of a statement.
My neighbor drives a bus.

Use a question mark at the end of a question.
How do you get to Park Street?

Use an exclamation point at the end of an exclamation or command.
Wow! That's amazing!
Give me that, now!

Commas

Use commas to separate items in a series.
We got pencils, pens, and crayons.

Use commas in dates.
School is closed on Monday, May 27, 2013.

Use a comma after the opening of a friendly letter and after the closing of any letter.
Dear Mary,
Your friend,

Apostrophes

Use apostrophes in contractions.
can not ...... can't
has not ...... hasn't
will not ...... won't

Use apostrophes to show who owns something.
a dog's collar
the boys' wallets
teacher's desk

Language Arts Practice

Read the passage. Then answer the questions. Darken the circle by the correct answer.

(1) My family and I love holidays. (2) We think Thanksgiving is the best. (3) Grandpa and Grandma come to our house. (4) First, we sits at a very long table. (5) Then, my sister brings in the food. (6) The turkey always tastes great! (7) After dinner we sing songs. (8) After dinner we play games. (9) Me can't wait for the next holiday!

1. Read sentence 4.

> First, we <u>sits</u> at a very long table.

What is the correct way to write the underlined verb?

(A) sitting

(B) sat

(C) sit

2. What is the **best** way to combine sentences 7 and 8?

(A) After dinner we sing songs and play games.

(B) After dinner we sing songs, play games.

(C) After dinner we sing songs after games.

3. What is the correct way to write sentence 9?

(A) Myself can't wait for the next holiday!

(B) I can't wait for the next holiday!

(C) correct as is

Name _____ Date _____

Read the passage. Then answer the questions. Darken the circle by the correct answer.

(1) Many birds visited my backyard. (2) The cardinals were red. (3) The cardinals made nests in our bushes. (4) I seen tiny hummingbirds too. (5) Them buzzed around the flowers in our garden. (6) Robins chirped sweetly to wake me in the morning.

4. Read these sentences.

> The cardinals were red.
> The cardinals made nests in our bushes.

What is the correct way to combine the sentences?

Ⓐ The cardinals made nests in our red bushes.

Ⓑ The cardinals made red nests in our bushes.

Ⓒ The red cardinals made nests in our bushes.

5. What is the correct way to write sentence 4?

Ⓐ I sees tiny hummingbirds too.

Ⓑ I seeing tiny hummingbirds too.

Ⓒ I saw tiny hummingbirds too.

6. Read sentence 5.

> <u>Them</u> buzzed around the flowers in our garden.

What is the correct way to write the underlined pronoun?

Ⓐ They

Ⓑ Their

Ⓒ Themselves

Name _____ Date _____

Read the passage. Then answer the questions. Darken the circle by the correct answer.

(1) Supermarkets sell food that comes from faraway places. (2) They use modern transportation. (3) The food is sent by plane, train, truck, and ship. (4) Loafies of bread might come from a bakery across town. (5) A group of bananas comes from across an ocean. (6) Food is sent from all over the United States and Mexico. (7) If they don't not use modern transportation, stores could only sell food from nearby farms.

7. What is the correct way to write sentence 4?

Ⓐ Loafs of bread might come from a bakery across town.

Ⓑ Loaves of bread might come from a bakery across town.

Ⓒ correct as is

8. What is the correct way to write the underlined part of sentence 5?

A <u>group of bananas</u> comes from across an ocean.

Ⓐ banana's group

Ⓑ herd of bananas

Ⓒ bunch of bananas

9. What is the correct way to write sentence 7?

Ⓐ If they don't use no modern transportation, stores could only sell food from nearby farms.

Ⓑ If they don't use modern transportation, stores could only sell food from nearby farms.

Ⓒ If they don't use none modern transportation, stores could only sell food from nearby farms.

© HMH Supplemental Publishers Inc.
© Houghton Mifflin Harcourt Publishing Company

Name _____ Date _____

Darken the circle by the correct answer.

10. What verb correctly completes the sentence?

| Yesterday the boys _____ tag. |

Ⓐ is playing

Ⓑ played

Ⓒ plays

11. What word completes the sentence?

| A lion has many sharp _____. |

Ⓐ teeth

Ⓑ tooth

Ⓒ toothes

12. Read these sentences.

| Andy talks. Andy tells jokes. |

What is the **best** way to combine them?

Ⓐ Andy talks and Andy tells jokes.

Ⓑ Andy jokes, tells, and talks.

Ⓒ Andy talks and tells jokes.

13. Which word stands for the underlined word?

| Joan has a new puppy. |

Ⓐ She

Ⓑ Her

Ⓒ They

14. Choose the complete sentence.

Ⓐ Is making a nest.

Ⓑ The making a nest.

Ⓒ The bird is making a nest.

© HMH Supplemental Publishers Inc.
© Houghton Mifflin Harcourt Publishing Company

Language Arts and Vocabulary Test Tips and Practice
Higher Scores on Reading and Language Arts, Grade 2

Darken the circle by the correct answer.

15. What describing word **best** completes this sentence?

> The boat sailed in the _____ water.

- Ⓐ swam
- Ⓑ blue
- Ⓒ waves

16. What describing word **best** completes this sentence?

> The kite flew _____ in the sky.

- Ⓐ string
- Ⓑ fell
- Ⓒ high

17. Which verb correctly completes this sentence?

> Where _____ Max and Ana going?

- Ⓐ was
- Ⓑ is
- Ⓒ are

18. Which verb correctly completes this sentence?

> Tamara _____ to the zoo.

- Ⓐ goes
- Ⓑ goed
- Ⓒ go

19. Which word can take the place of the underlined word?

> Have you seen <u>Brian's</u> baseball glove?

- Ⓐ their
- Ⓑ his
- Ⓒ our

© HMH Supplemental Publishers Inc.
© Houghton Mifflin Harcourt Publishing Company

Read the passage. Then answer the questions. Darken the circle by the correct answer.

(1) I got a book of stories from the library. (2) The book's title is <u>Elephants</u>. (3) My favorite story in the book is called "Fun at the Zoo" (4) Its a story about a boy and a girl at a zoo. (5) There is also a funny story about a family's trip to see elephants in tennessee. (6) It made me laugh out loud!

20. What is the correct way to write sentence 3?

Ⓐ My favorite story in the book is called "Fun at the Zoo"?

Ⓑ My favorite story, in the book is called "Fun, at the Zoo"

Ⓒ My favorite story in the book is called "Fun at the Zoo."

21. What is the correct way to write sentence 4?

Ⓐ Its' a story about a boy and a girl at a zoo.

Ⓑ It's a story about a boy and a girl at a zoo.

Ⓒ correct as is

22. Which word in sentence 5 needs a capital letter?

Ⓐ funny

Ⓑ trip

Ⓒ tennessee

Name _____ Date _____

Read the letter Tevy got from his uncle. Then answer the questions. Darken the circle by the correct answer.

Dear Tevy

(1) I am in Thailand. (2) I took a trek, or walk, through a beautiful forest to a small village. (3) I spent new year's day in the village. (4) Then I took a train to Bangkok, the capital city of Thailand. (5) On the way, I stopped at a park and saw interesting animals. (6) I saw elephants oxen and barking deer. (7) I miss you.

Love,

Uncle Jack

23. Which punctuation mark belongs after "Dear Tevy"?

Ⓐ a period

Ⓑ a comma

Ⓒ an exclamation mark

24. Which words in sentence 3 need to be capitalized?

Ⓐ New Year's Day

Ⓑ I Spent

Ⓒ The Village

25. What is the correct way to write sentence 6?

Ⓐ I saw elephants, oxen, and barking deer.

Ⓑ I saw, elephants oxen and, barking deer.

Ⓒ correct as is

© HMH Supplemental Publishers Inc.
© Houghton Mifflin Harcourt Publishing Company

Name _____   Date _____

Read the passage. Then answer the questions. Darken the circle by the correct answer.

(1) Patty was reading the newspaper. (2) The date on the front was Wednesday March 7. (3) Mrs. Parker said, "I thought today was Tuesday. (4) What will I do now (5) Ive lost a day!"

(6) "Today is Tuesday," said Patty. (7) She held up her newspaper and said that it was from last week.

26. What is the correct way to write sentence 2?

Ⓐ The date on the front was Wednesday–March 7.

Ⓑ The date on the front was Wednesday, March 7.

Ⓒ The date on the front was Wednesday, March, 7.

27. What punctuation mark belongs at the end of sentence 4?

Ⓐ .

Ⓑ !

Ⓒ ?

28. What is the correct way to write sentence 5?

Ⓐ I've lost a day!"

Ⓑ Iv'e lost a day!"

Ⓒ I'v lost a day!"

© HMH Supplemental Publishers Inc.
© Houghton Mifflin Harcourt Publishing Company

Language Arts and Vocabulary Test Tips and Practice
Higher Scores on Reading and Language Arts, Grade 2

Darken the circle by the correct answer.

29. Which correctly spelled word fits the sentence?

> It _____ raining in the afternoon.

Ⓐ stoped

Ⓑ stopped

Ⓒ stopt

30. Which word is misspelled?

> My baby <u>sister</u> <u>cryed</u> when her <u>balloon</u> broke.

Ⓐ sister

Ⓑ cryed

Ⓒ balloon

31. What is the correct ending punctuation for this sentence?

> Ouch, that hurts

Ⓐ .

Ⓑ !

Ⓒ ?

32. Choose the sentence that is correct.

Ⓐ Would you read me another story.

Ⓑ Would you read me another story?

Ⓒ Would you read me another story,

33. Choose the sentence that is correct.

Ⓐ My first plane ride was on March 7, 2012.

Ⓑ My first plane ride was on March 7 2012.

Ⓒ My first plane ride was on March 7. 2012.

© HMH Supplemental Publishers Inc.
© Houghton Mifflin Harcourt Publishing Company

Darken the circle by the correct answer.

34. Choose the sentence that is correct.

   Ⓐ The girls on Elena's soccer team picked a team name.

   Ⓑ The girls' on Elenas soccer team picked a team name.

   Ⓒ The girls on Elena soccer team picked a team name.

35. What correctly spelled word fits the sentence?

> My father took a
> _____ of the baby.

   Ⓐ pichure

   Ⓑ pickture

   Ⓒ picture

36. Choose the sentence that has correct punctuation and capitalization.

   Ⓐ aunt Julie is very nice.

   Ⓑ Where are your gloves?

   Ⓒ Can you ride a horse

37. Choose the sentence that has correct punctuation and capitalization.

   Ⓐ This is my sister gail.

   Ⓑ She goes to Bluefield High School.

   Ⓒ Do you have a big Sister!

38. Mark the sentence that has correct punctuation and capitalization.

   Ⓐ I'm going to a movie on Saturday.

   Ⓑ Would you like to come with me.

   Ⓒ Was'nt that fun?

Taking Vocabulary Tests

In the Vocabulary Tips and Practice section, you will review common vocabulary skills and terms. You will read about strategies for answering different kinds of vocabulary questions. Next, you will be asked to read passages and answer vocabulary questions. You will also be asked to answer stand-alone questions.

Test Tips for Vocabulary

Using Context Clues

One way to figure out the meaning of a word is to use **context clues**. These are words and sentences around the word. Use the following steps to answer questions about words you do not know:

Step 1: Read the sentence that contains the unknown word. See if the words before or after it give clues to the word's meaning. Then read sentences around the word and look for clues.

Step 2: Use the clues to guess the word's meaning.

Step 3: Check your answer by using it in the sentence in place of the unknown word.

Using Word Parts

Many words are made up of word parts. A **root word** is a word that does not have any prefixes or suffixes added. For example, the root word of teacher is teach. A **prefix** is added to the beginning of a word to make a new word. A prefix changes the meaning of the root word. A **suffix** is added to the end of a word to create a new word. A suffix changes the meaning of the root word.

Prefixes

Prefix	Meaning
re-	again
un-	not, the opposite of

Prefix		Root Word		New Word	Meaning
re	+	fill	=	refill	fill again
un	+	able	=	unable	not able

Suffixes

Suffix	Meaning
-or, -er	one who
-ly	in a certain way
-less	without

Root Word		Suffix		New Word	Meaning
act	+	or	=	actor	one who acts
bake	+	er	=	baker	one who bakes
nice	+	ly	=	nicely	in a nice way
name	+	less	=	nameless	without a name

Identifying Antonyms and Synonyms

Antonyms are words that have opposite meanings.
 night and day
 in and out

Synonyms are words with the same or nearly the same meaning.
 yell and scream
 tiny and little and small

Analyzing Multiple-Meaning Words

Some words have more than one meaning. To decide on the correct meaning of a multiple-meaning word, think about whether it is a noun or a verb. Then read the words and sentences around it to look for clues.

I put the red **rose** in a vase. [Rose is a noun. Clues are "red" and "vase." Rose means "a kind of flower."]

The sun **rose** at 7:00 in the morning. [Rose is a verb. Clues are "sun" and "morning." Rose means "came up."]

Use these steps to decide on the correct meaning of a multiple-meaning word:

Step 1: Think about whether the word is a noun or a verb.

Step 2: Read the words and sentences around it to look for clues.

Step 3: Check your definition to see if it makes sense in the sentence.

Compound Words

Compound words are made up of two smaller words. To find the meaning of most compound words, put together the meanings of the smaller words.

Compound Word		Smaller Words	Meaning
backyard	=	back + yard	yard in the back
blackbird	=	black + bird	bird that is black

Vocabulary Practice

Read the poem. Then answer the questions. Darken the circle by the correct answer.

>First a seed so tiny
>>Hidden from our sight;
>Then two tiny little leaves
>>Looking for the light;
>
>Soon a bud appears
>>And then a pretty flower,
>Touched by golden sunshine,
>>Washed by a silver shower;
>
>Growing prettier and prettier,
>>Hour by hour!
>Touched by golden sunshine,
>>Washed by a silver shower.

1. Read these lines from the poem.

> Then two tiny little <u>leaves</u>
> Looking for the light;

Which sentence uses <u>leaves</u> the **same** way it is used in the poem?

Ⓐ Six take away two leaves four.

Ⓑ Tad always leaves the door open.

Ⓒ Rosa leaves for school at 7:30.

Ⓓ In the fall, the leaves fall off the tree.

2. Read this line from the poem.

> Touched by golden <u>sunshine</u>,

What does the compound word <u>sunshine</u> mean?

Ⓐ when the skin turns red from the sun

Ⓑ the light coming from the sun

Ⓒ the sun coming up in the morning

Ⓓ the sun going down in the evening

3. Read this line from the poem.

> Washed by a silver <u>shower</u>.

What word means **almost the same** as <u>shower</u>?

Ⓐ rain

Ⓑ ring

Ⓒ bathtub

Ⓓ soap

Name _____ Date _____

Read the passage. Then answer the questions. Darken the circle by the correct answer.

Did you know that owls are good hunters? Owls sleep all day long. At night they wake up and fly around. They look for mice to eat. Owls have huge eyes. Their large eyes let in more light. Owls can see better at night than we can. Owls also hear very well. They can even hear a mouse running in the grass. They can fly without making any noise at all. All these things make owls good hunters.

4. What word in the passage means the **opposite** of sleep?

Ⓐ day

Ⓑ long

Ⓒ wake

Ⓓ see

5. Choose the word that **best** completes the sentence.

An owl has _____ hearing.

Ⓐ good

Ⓑ okay

Ⓒ fine

Ⓓ excellent

6. Read these sentences from the story.

Owls have huge eyes. Their large eyes let in more light. Owls can see better at night than we can.

What clue word helps the reader know what huge means?

Ⓐ eyes

Ⓑ large

Ⓒ light

Ⓓ better

Name _____ Date _____

Darken the circle by the correct answer.

7. Read the sentence.

> The girls play in the sand at the <u>seashore</u>.

What does the word <u>seashore</u> mean?

Ⓐ air by the sea

Ⓑ land by the sea

Ⓒ road by the sea

Ⓓ swimming by the sea

8. Read the sentence.

> She walked <u>slowly</u> to the front of the room.

The word <u>slowly</u> means

Ⓐ in a slow way.

Ⓑ too slow.

Ⓒ not slow.

Ⓓ the opposite of slow.

© HMH Supplemental Publishers Inc.
© Houghton Mifflin Harcourt Publishing Company

Darken the circle by the correct answer.

9. Which definition of <u>long</u> is used in the sentence below?

> **long** (long)
>
> *verb*
>   1. to want very much
>
> *adjective*
>   2. having great length
>
> *adjective*
>   3. lasting a long time
>
> *adverb*
>   4. from the beginning
>   to the end

The <u>long</u> river stretched across the entire state.

Ⓐ definition 1

Ⓑ definition 2

Ⓒ definition 3

Ⓓ definition 4

10. Read the sentence.

I was so <u>glad</u> when I saw all the good grades on my report card.

What word means the **opposite** of <u>glad</u>?

Ⓐ happy

Ⓑ quiet

Ⓒ unhappy

Ⓓ silly

Darken the circle by the correct answer.

11. Which word belongs in this group?

> great, amazing, super, _____

Ⓐ poor

Ⓑ rotten

Ⓒ terrible

Ⓓ wonderful

12. Read the sentences.

> Ms. Ling walked in the classroom. Some children were laughing and talking. Some were playing. Ms. Ling said, "Stop this <u>monkey business</u> and get back to work!"

The words <u>monkey business</u> mean

Ⓐ fooling around.

Ⓑ selling monkeys.

Ⓒ hanging from trees.

Ⓓ eating bananas.

© HMH Supplemental Publishers Inc.
© Houghton Mifflin Harcourt Publishing Company

Name _____ Date _____

Darken the circle by the correct answer.

13. Mark the word with a meaning that fits both sentences.

> Please _____ me that book.
>
> What does the minute _____ on the clock say?

Ⓐ give

Ⓑ sell

Ⓒ find

Ⓓ hand

14. Which word is the **best** clue about the meaning of the word <u>dozen</u>?

> The baker asked for a dozen eggs. I gave her twelve fresh eggs.

Ⓐ baker

Ⓑ eggs

Ⓒ twelve

Ⓓ fresh

15. Read the sentence.

> The squirrel ran up the <u>high</u> tree.

What word means **almost the same** as <u>high</u>?

Ⓐ lonely

Ⓑ tall

Ⓒ leaves

Ⓓ low

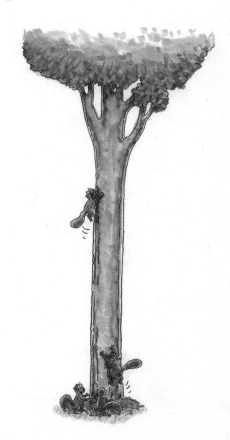

Darken the circle by the correct answer.

16. Choose the word with a meaning that fits both groups of underlined words.

> <u>water at the ocean</u> or <u>to make a hand signal</u>

- Ⓐ seen
- Ⓑ sail
- Ⓒ clap
- Ⓓ wave

17. What is the root word of <u>rebuild</u>?

- Ⓐ build
- Ⓑ bill
- Ⓒ return
- Ⓓ boil

18. Which definition of <u>bear</u> is used in the sentence below?

> **bear (bair)**
>
> *verb*
>   1. to carry
>
> *noun*
>   2. a large animal with thick fur and strong claws
>
> *verb*
>   3. to bring forth, as in fruit
>
> *verb*
>   4. to be able to stand pain

> The <u>bear</u> caught a fish in the stream.

- Ⓐ definition 1
- Ⓑ definition 2
- Ⓒ definition 3
- Ⓓ definition 4

Writing
Test Tips and Practice

Taking Writing Tests

In the Writing Tips and Practice section, you will learn how your writing will be scored. You will also read some tips that will help you respond to writing prompts. Look over the graphic organizers that you can use to help you plan your writing. Then, you will practice responding to some writing prompts.

Scoring the Writing Prompts

The writing prompts will be scored on a 4-point scale. The writing prompts will be scored for content, organization, and conventions. If a response is off-topic, cannot be read, makes no sense, has too little information to be scored, or is blank, it will not receive any score. Ask your parent or teacher if you need help understanding this 4-point scale.

SCORING ON A 4-POINT SCALE:

A **4-*point*** response demonstrates **advanced** success with the writing task. The essay:
• focuses consistently on the topic
• shows effective organization throughout, with smooth transitions
• offers thoughtful ideas
• develops ideas thoroughly, using examples and details
• shows good control of written language

A **3-*point*** response demonstrates **competent** success with the writing task. In general, the essay:
• focuses mostly on the topic
• shows effective organization, with minor lapses
• offers mostly thoughtful ideas
• develops ideas adequately and uses some general and some specific reasons and evidence
• shows general control of written language

A **2-*point*** response demonstrates **limited** success with the writing task. In general, the essay:

- includes some ideas that are related to the topic but does not focus consistently on the topic
- shows some organization, with noticeable gaps in the logical flow of ideas
- offers predictable ideas
- develops or supports ideas with little elaboration and reasoning
- shows limited control of written language

A **1-*point*** response demonstrates **emerging** effort with the writing task. In general, the essay:

- shows little awareness of the topic
- lacks organization
- offers confusing ideas
- develops ideas in a minimal way, if at all, or gives only a few reasons
- shows major problems with control of written language

Tips for Responding to a Prompt

- First, **read the prompt carefully**. Be sure that you understand exactly what the prompt is asking.
- **Decide who your audience is. You should ask yourself, "Who is going to read this?"** You might write differently for a friend than you would write to the school principal. Some prompts will tell you who the audience is.
- Next, **decide on your topic.** It is good to choose one topic to write about. Make sure when you write that your topic is stated as your main idea. Then make sure all the details and events stay on that one topic. Some prompts will tell you what topic to write about.

- Before you begin writing, **plan**. This is a good time to use a graphic organizer to plan what you want to write. This is the time to think about what you want to say before you begin writing your response.
- Write in **complete sentences.** Make sure your sentences and paragraphs flow smoothly. Sentences should support the main idea. They should be arranged in an order that makes sense to the reader. Use time order words like *first*, *next*, and *last* if necessary. Also, remember to write neatly.
- Finally, **proofread your response.** Check for spelling and punctuation errors. Make sure each sentence has a subject and verb. Look over verb tenses to see if you have used them correctly. Make your edits as neat as possible.

These tips can help you do well on the writing section of tests. Remember that practice makes perfect. Read and write as often as possible so your reading and writing get better and better.

Graphic Organizers

Writing Details

A Web is helpful when thinking about details. Write your topic in the middle circle. Then write words or phrases that come to mind about the topic in the outer circles.

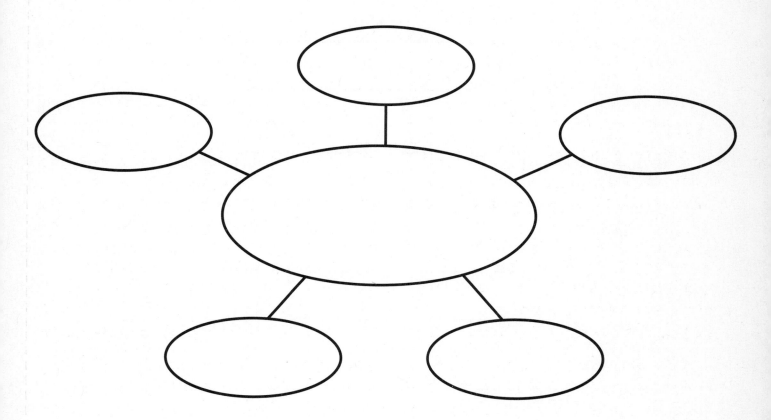

© HMH Supplemental Publishers Inc.
© Houghton Mifflin Harcourt Publishing Company

Name _____   Date _____

Sequence of Events

A Sequence of Events organizer can help you put story events or steps in correct order. Use the time order words *first*, *next*, *then*, and *last* in your writing to help the reader understand the order in which events happen.

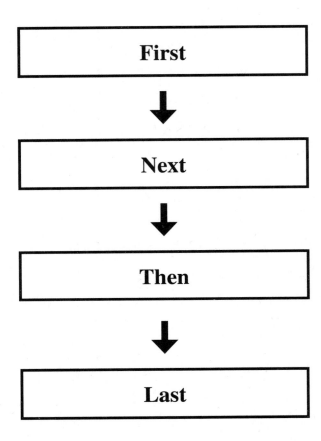

Main Idea and Details

All of the details in a paragraph need to tell about the main idea or topic of the paragraph. A Main Idea and Details chart can help you keep in mind your topic and make sure all the details you write stick to the topic.

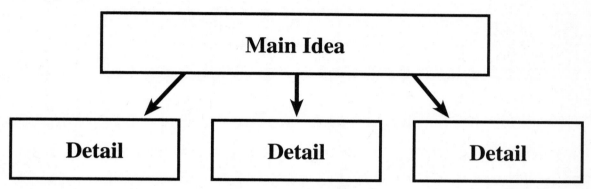

Compare and Contrast

When you compare and contrast two things, you tell how they are alike and different. A Venn Diagram like the one below can help you sort how two things are alike and different. Write about one thing in one circle, about the other thing in the second circle, and how they are alike in the middle.

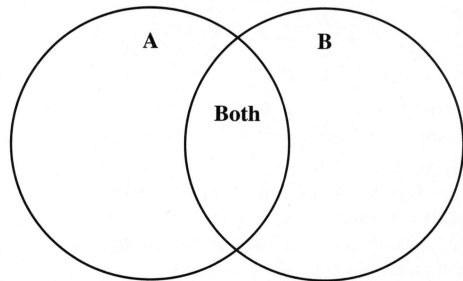

Name _____ Date _____

Plan your writing. Write your response. Then, proofread what you have written.

What is your favorite book? Tell the name of this book. Explain to a friend why you like it.

As you write your response, be sure to

• Write about only one book.
• Include at least two reasons you like it.
• Give details that support your reasons.
• Include an introduction, a middle, and an ending.
• Write in complete sentences.

Prewriting

1. **Read the prompt.** Read the prompt carefully. Think about who your audience is. Think about your topic.

Purpose. In the prompt, you are asked to tell a friend about your favorite book. The prompt tells you your audience. It tells you what you will write about.

Complete the following sentences:

My audience is

_____

_____

I am going to write about

_____

_____

_____

2. **Plan.** As you write, you want to describe your book. Use the map below to list details you want to include in your writing.

Write the name of your favorite book in the center circle. Then write details you like about the book in the circles around the name.

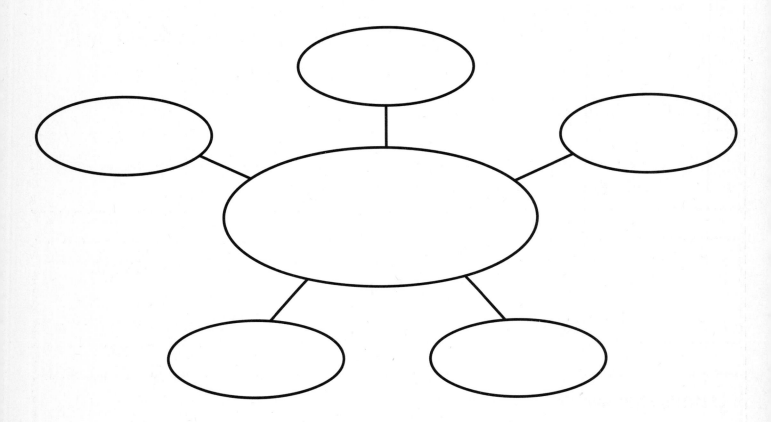

3. **Organize Your Writing.** As you write, you want to describe your details. You will want to organize your thoughts so that you can present them logically to your audience.

In the organizer below, fill in your favorite book title in the first sentence. Then add some reasons this book is your favorite. Use the details that you wrote in the web on page 72. Finally, add any other details that support these reasons. You might want to tell details from the book that support a reason it is your favorite.

My favorite book is _____ .

One reason I like it:	Another reason I like it:
_____	_____

Details that support this reason:	Details that support this reason:
1. _____	1. _____
2. _____	2. _____

Writing, Editing, and Revising

1. **Draft Your Response.** Now you will write a first draft of your response on your own paper. Remember, it must have an introduction and an ending. Use the graphic organizer below as a guide.

Introduction
Begin by stating the name of your favorite book in a complete sentence.
Middle
Give one reason you like it. Then give details that support your reason. State another reason you like it. Give details that support that reason.
Ending
End by stating the name of your favorite book in a complete sentence. Tell your audience what they should do next.

2. **Edit Your Response.** Now you will read your response. Ask yourself these questions about your writing.

    • Does your response have a clear introduction sentence? Does it name your favorite book?

    • Is your response organized? Does it give reasons why the book is your favorite?

    • Do you give supporting details for your reasons?

    • Do you repeat the same words? Can you change any words to clearer, more descriptive words?

    • Did you write a clear ending sentence? Did it name your favorite book?

    • Did you remember your audience? Did you write your response to one friend?

3. **Revise Your Response.** Look over the first draft of your response and the edits you have made. Make changes to your response. Rewrite all or part of it on your own paper.

4.   **Write Your Response.** On your own paper, write a final response. Write clearly. Use complete sentences.

> What is your favorite book? Tell the name of this book. Explain to a friend why you like this book.

5.   **Proofread Your Response.** Go back to your final response and use this checklist to check your work one last time.

_____ I named my favorite book in my first sentence.

_____ I gave reasons why I like the book.

_____ I used only complete sentences.

_____ I used correct capitalization.

_____ I used correct punctuation.

_____ I used correct spelling.

Writing Prompt 2: Informative

Plan your writing. Write your response. Then, proofread what you have written.

Make believe you have invented a new game. Give your game a name. Write directions to tell your friends how to play this game.

As you write your response, be sure to

- Write about only one game.
- Write directions in order.
- Give details that make your writing clear.
- Write in complete sentences.

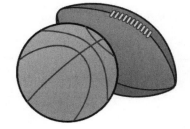

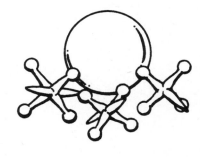

Prewriting

1. **Read the prompt.** Read the prompt carefully. Think about who your audience is. Think about your topic.

Purpose. In the prompt, you are asked to explain how to play a make-believe game. The prompt tells you your audience.

Complete the following sentences:

My audience is

_____

_____

I am going to write about

_____

_____

_____

_____

© HMH Supplemental Publishers Inc.
© Houghton Mifflin Harcourt Publishing Company

2. **Plan.** As you write, you want to tell how to play the game. Use the chart below to organize your game directions.

Write the name of your game on the line. Then write your steps in the boxes. Decide on the best order for your steps. Number the boxes in the correct order.

_____

Step _____

Step _____

Step _____

Step _____

3. **Organize Your Writing.** As you write, you want to begin by telling your topic, which is the name of your game. Describe what the game is like.

Then explain how to play the game by writing the steps in order. It can help to picture each step in your mind as you write. Use the steps you wrote on page 79. Use the clue words *first*, *next*, *then*, and *last* to help tell the order.

Opening sentences:
Have you ever played _____? It is a _____ game.

First,

Next,

Then,

Last,

Writing, Editing, and Revising

1. **Draft Your Response.** Now you will write a first draft of your response on your own paper. Remember, it must have an introduction and an ending. Use the graphic organizer below as a guide.

Introduction
Begin by telling the name of your game and one thing about it.
Middle
Tell how to play the game. Be sure to tell the steps in the correct order.
Ending
End by telling your friends why they might like to play this game.

2.   **Edit Your Response.** Now you will read your response. Ask yourself these questions about your writing.

- Is the game clearly identified in the introduction?

- Have you pictured yourself playing the game in your mind?

- What step comes first? Next? Last?

- Have you used the clue words *first*, *next*, *then*, and *last* to let your readers know the correct order of steps?

- Did you end with a sentence that would make your friends want to play the game?

3.   **Revise Your Response.** Look over the first draft of your response and the edits you have made. Make changes to your response. Rewrite all or part of it on your own paper.

4. **Write Your Response.** On your own paper, write a final response. Write clearly. Use complete sentences.

> Make believe you have invented a new game. Give your game a name. Write directions to tell your friends how to play this game.

5. **Proofread Your Response.** Go back to your final response and use this checklist to check your work one last time.

_____ I named my game in my first sentences.

_____ I described the steps in the correct order.

_____ I used only complete sentences.

_____ I used strong, active verbs.

_____ I used correct punctuation.

_____ I used correct spelling.

Writing Prompt 3: Narrative

Plan your writing. Write your response. Then, proofread what you have written.

> Write a story for your friends about a family who moves to your neighborhood. The family has a child your age that needs a friend.

As you write your response, be sure to

- Describe where the story takes place.
- Describe the characters in the story.
- Tell your story events in order.
- Decide what the problem is and how it will be solved.

Name _____   Date _____

Prewriting

1.   **Read the prompt.** Read the prompt carefully. Think about who your audience is. Think about your story topic.

Purpose. In the prompt, you are asked to tell a story for your friends about a new family in your neighborhood and a child your age that needs a friend.

Complete the following sentences:

My audience is

_____

_____

I am going to write about

_____

_____

_____

_____

© HMH Supplemental Publishers Inc.
© Houghton Mifflin Harcourt Publishing Company

2. **Plan.** As you write, you want to include details about the place and the people. Use the chart below to decide what the problem is and how it will be solved.

Who is in the story?
Where does the story take place?
What is the problem?
How is the problem solved?

3. **Organize Your Writing.** As you write, you want to tell your story in order. Use the chart on page 86 to help you fill in the story map below.

Beginning
Middle (problem)
1.
2.
3.
4.
End (solution to problem)
1.
2.

Writing, Editing, and Revising

1. **Draft Your Response.** Now you will write a first draft of your story on your own paper. Your story should have a clear beginning, middle, and end. Remember to include many details about the place, the people, the events, the problem, and the solution. Use the graphic organizer below as a guide.

Beginning
Describe the setting and the characters.

Middle
Tell what the problem is. Be sure to tell events in order.

Ending
Tell how the problem is solved.

2.   **Edit Your Response.** Now you will read your response. Ask yourself these questions about your writing.

- What details tell about the setting and characters?
- What details show what happened? What details can you add to make events clearer?
- Does the problem feel like something that could really happen?
- Is it clear how the characters work out their problem?
- Does your story have a beginning, a middle, and an end?

3.   **Revise Your Response.** Look over the first draft of your response and the edits you have made. Make changes to your response. Rewrite all or part of it on your own paper.

4. **Write Your Response.** On your own paper, write a final response. Write clearly. Use complete sentences.

> Write a story about a family who moves to your neighborhood. The family has a child your age that needs a friend.

5. **Proofread Your Response.** Go back to your final response and use this checklist to check your work one last time.

_____ I described the setting and characters.

_____ I described the story events in the correct order.

_____ I used only complete sentences.

_____ I used good describing words.

_____ I used quotation marks and other punctuation correctly.

_____ I used correct spelling.

Reading
Practice Test

Read the passage. Then answer the questions. For multiple-choice items, darken the circle by the correct answer. For the open-ended item, write the answer.

Dear Wanda,

    I haven't had one chance to write you for the past three months. I have been very busy in school. But now that school is over, I want to tell you what I have been doing.

    I played on my school's softball team this spring. We won most of our games. Best of all, we traveled to different cities to play other teams. That was fun!

    I have a big surprise for you. My mother gave me a new puppy for my birthday. My puppy is brown and black with a long tail and a white spot on her forehead. I named her Melissa. I can't wait for you to see her. When are you coming to visit this summer? Please write to me soon.

Your cousin,

Alice

1. Why does the passage begin with "Dear Wanda"?

   Ⓐ It is a letter to Wanda.

   Ⓑ It is a heading about the section.

   Ⓒ It is the title of the story.

   Ⓓ It is the name of the author.

2. What is the main idea of the first paragraph?

   Ⓐ Wanda and Alice are cousins.

   Ⓑ School is over for this school year.

   Ⓒ Alice has been too busy to write.

   Ⓓ Alice hasn't written for three months.

3. What did Alice get for her birthday?

   Ⓐ a softball

   Ⓑ a puppy

   Ⓒ a trip

   Ⓓ a new friend

4. The picture shows how Alice

   Ⓐ felt on her birthday.

   Ⓑ plays with her dog.

   Ⓒ takes care of Melissa.

   Ⓓ feels about Wanda.

5. Which word from the letter shows how Wanda feels about playing softball?

Ⓐ busy

Ⓑ won

Ⓒ traveled

Ⓓ fun

6. Alice would like Wanda to come visit

Ⓐ this summer.

Ⓑ in three months.

Ⓒ when school is over.

Ⓓ after a softball game.

7. List two ways the author shows that Wanda lives far away from Alice.

_____

_____

_____

_____

Read the story. Then answer the questions. For multiple-choice items, darken the circle by the correct answer. For the open-ended item, write the answer.

The Puppet Show

Lonzell and Marta are excited. Today they are going to put on a puppet show for the other children in their class. Malcolm is in the show, too, but he isn't excited. He is nervous. He's never been in a puppet show before.

Marta and Lonzell are going to work the puppets while Malcolm reads the lines. He is worried that he won't read the lines right.

"Don't worry, Malcolm," Marta tells him before the show. "You'll do great."

Lonzell pats Malcolm on the shoulder. "You did well in practice. The show will go just as well," he says.

Malcolm tries to smile at his friends, but he still feels nervous. He wonders how Lonzell and Marta can seem so calm.

Lonzell, Marta, and Malcolm go behind the stage to get ready for the show.

Their teacher introduces the show and tells the children to listen quietly.

Marta and Lonzell raise their puppets. Now, it is time for Malcolm to start reading. His throat is dry. He opens his mouth. Nothing comes out. Lonzell turns to look at him.

"You can do it," Lonzell whispers.

Malcolm takes a deep breath. He reminds himself that he did well in practice. He can do this. He opens his mouth, and this time the words come out. He keeps reading. Before he knows it, the children in the audience are clapping happily.

Malcolm has done it! He's made it through the whole show.

"That was fun," Marta says.

"I hope we can do another show soon," Lonzell adds.

Malcolm smiles at his friends. "Me, too," he says.

8. How is Malcolm different at the end of the story from the way he was at the beginning of the story?

Ⓐ He cries because the show is over.

Ⓑ He wants to act in another show.

Ⓒ He promises to practice for the show.

Ⓓ He is nervous about the show.

9. Why did Lonzell, Marta, and Malcolm go behind the stage?

Ⓐ to get ready for the show

Ⓑ to make their puppets

Ⓒ to make Malcolm feel better

Ⓓ to leave Malcolm alone

10. What lesson did Malcolm learn?

Ⓐ Slow but sure wins the race.

Ⓑ Don't put all your eggs in one basket.

Ⓒ Better late than never.

Ⓓ Believe in yourself.

11. Why wouldn't the children in the audience know that Malcolm was nervous?

Ⓐ The teacher told the children that he is calm.

Ⓑ They couldn't see him behind the puppet stage.

Ⓒ Lonzell did all the talking on the stage.

Ⓓ Marta's puppet kept the children happy.

12. What is the **best** summary of the story?

   (A) Malcolm organized a puppet show. He liked to read aloud. Malcolm read the lines for the puppets and the show was a success.

   (B) Lonzell, Marta, and Malcolm were excited. Lonzell patted Malcolm on the shoulder. Soon Malcolm's throat was dry and he could not talk.

   (C) Malcolm was nervous about the puppet show. Lonzell reminded Malcolm that he had done well in practice. Knowing how well he had done in practice helped Malcolm do a good job in the show.

   (D) There was going to be a puppet show. Marta and Lonzell were ready to go. The teacher told the children to listen quietly. Malcolm did not talk. They waited for the show to begin.

13. Who is telling this story?

   (A) a narrator who is not named

   (B) Marta

   (C) Lonzell

   (D) Malcolm

14. Complete the chart to show what each character's job is in the puppet show.

Character	Job in the Puppet Show
Teacher	introduce the show
Marta	work a puppet
Lonzell	
Malcolm	

Name _____ Date _____

Read the poem. Then answer the questions. For multiple-choice items, darken the circle by the correct answer. For the open-ended item, write the answer.

The Acrobat

The cat tiptoes across
the back of the couch
like an acrobat
on a high wire.

With no net below
(in case of falls)
she holds her tail up—
a feather curling
toward the circus top,
and her whiskers out—
a pole for balance.

At the end
she hops quickly
onto the lamp table
as if that balancing act
had been a Sunday walk.

15. The poet compares the cat to a

Ⓐ circus performer.

Ⓑ balancing pole.

Ⓒ couch.

Ⓓ feather.

16. The phrase "a feather curling toward the circus top" describes the cat's

Ⓐ whiskers.

Ⓑ tail.

Ⓒ walk.

Ⓓ feet.

© HMH Supplemental Publishers Inc.
© Houghton Mifflin Harcourt Publishing Company

17. Why is the poem set with short lines of text?

Ⓐ to fit on the page

Ⓑ to end each sentence

Ⓒ to show the rhyme

Ⓓ to show the rhythm

18. What is another good name for this poem?

Ⓐ A Falling Star

Ⓑ On a Sunday Walk

Ⓒ Circus Cat

Ⓓ Funny Clown

19. What does the cat use to keep her balance?

Ⓐ the lamp table

Ⓑ her whiskers

Ⓒ the back of the couch

Ⓓ a pole

20. Read these lines.

> With no net below
> (in case of falls)
> she holds her tail up—

Why do you think the poet used mostly one-syllable words?

Ⓐ they are easy to spell

Ⓑ to make the lines rhyme

Ⓒ so they can be read with rhythm

Ⓓ because cat is a one-syllable word

21. How does the picture help the reader identify the setting of the poem?

_____

_____

_____

_____

_____

Read the passage. Then answer the questions. For multiple-choice items, darken the circle by the correct answer. For the open-ended item, write the answer.

Gator Holes

The Florida Everglades is a special place. It is home to many rare plants and animals. Visitors can see many unusual plants and animals there. The Everglades is not like any other place on Earth!

One animal is called "the keeper of the Everglades." This animal is the alligator. How do alligators help keep the Everglades in good shape? The places where they live, called "gator holes," are important.

A gator hole is usually made and kept clean by an alligator. When a gator finds a deep hole in the swamp, it gets to work. The gator uses its snout, or nose, and its claws to rip out all the plants and mud. The gator throws this material on the land around the hole.

Now the hole is clean. More water can fill it. More fish can live in it. When the dry season comes, much of the Everglades dries up. But gator holes still have water. Many animals come to the gator holes to live. Without gator holes, these animals would die.

All around the gator holes, plants grow. The plants like the rich mud made from the alligators' work. Over time, trees grow. Trees shade the plants and animals, protecting them from the sun!

Now you know why alligators are so important. Maybe some day you can see a gator hole for yourself!

22. Which sentence **best** tells what this passage is about?

Ⓐ The Everglades is full of plants and animals.

Ⓑ Alligators work on gator holes all the time.

Ⓒ Gator holes help living things in the Everglades.

Ⓓ An alligator uses its snout to rip out plants.

23. Why did the author **most likely** write "Gator Holes"?

Ⓐ to give facts about the Everglades

Ⓑ to tell a funny story about alligators

Ⓒ to get readers to go to Florida

Ⓓ to explain why alligators are important

© HMH Supplemental Publishers Inc.
© Houghton Mifflin Harcourt Publishing Company

24. Which sentence is true about gator holes?

Ⓐ Few plants grow around gator holes.

Ⓑ Alligators keep gator holes clean.

Ⓒ Gator holes are filled with plants and mud.

Ⓓ Only alligators live in gator holes.

25. Read the sentences from the passage.

> It is home to many <u>rare</u> plants and animals. Visitors can see many unusual plants and animals there.

What does it mean when plants and animals are <u>rare</u>?

Ⓐ They are not common.

Ⓑ They can be eaten safely.

Ⓒ They can be seen in many places.

Ⓓ They live only in the Everglades.

26. Which sentence from the passage supports the idea that alligators are important to the Everglades?

Ⓐ The Florida Everglades is a special place.

Ⓑ The Everglades is not like any other place on Earth!

Ⓒ Without gator holes, these animals would die.

Ⓓ Maybe some day you can see a gator hole for yourself!

27. If you wanted to see a gator hole, where would you **most likely** go?

Ⓐ to the Everglades

Ⓑ to a zoo

Ⓒ to a Florida beach

Ⓓ where trees grow

28. Number the events in the order that tells how a gator hole is made.

_____ The gator throws plants and mud around the hole.

_____ The gator uses its snout to pull out plants and mud.

_____ A gator finds a deep hole in a swamp.

_____ Water fills the hole.

Read the passage. Then answer the questions. For multiple-choice items, darken the circle by the correct answer. For the open-ended item, write the answer.

Pioneer Days

A Special Law

In 1862 President Lincoln signed a special law. It let pioneer families have land if they earned it. They had to live on the land and farm it for five years. It took lots of hard work to make the land a good place to live and farm. Everyone in a pioneer family had jobs to do.

Break of Dawn

A pioneer father got up very early in the morning. He went outside to feed the animals. He also got his tools ready for the day's work. He worked to clear the land. He cut down trees and tall grass so he could plant seeds.

A pioneer mother was busy too. She gathered eggs, made butter, and cooked breakfast on the fire. Many pioneer homes did not have ovens or stoves. Making breakfast took a long time!

Midday Work

Pioneer families spent the afternoon doing their jobs. The boys took care of the cattle and horses. They also helped take care of the crops. The girls made candles and soap. They made butter and cheese. They also learned to sew.

The women spun wool into yarn and made clothes. They also picked vegetables and got meat ready to store for winter. The men plowed the fields. They cut logs so the family would have firewood for winter.

Sundown

After supper, pioneer families spent time together. They had worked all day long. Now it was time to rest. They told stories and played games. Like parents today, pioneer parents probably gave their children cozy bear hugs and tucked them into bed at the end of the day!

Word Bank	
acre	a large area of land
chores	everyday jobs at home
crops	plants grown by people for food
pioneer	a person or group of people who are the first to live in a place

29. Which question is answered in the last paragraph of the passage?

Ⓐ What time did pioneer children go to bed?

Ⓑ What chores did pioneer families do at bedtime?

Ⓒ What did pioneer children do in the evening?

Ⓓ What did pioneer parents do after children went to bed?

30. Which section of the passage tells what pioneer families did in the morning?

Ⓐ A Special Law

Ⓑ Break of Dawn

Ⓒ Midday Work

Ⓓ Sundown

31. How does the Word Bank help a reader understand the passage?

Ⓐ It tells the meanings of words.

Ⓑ It tells how to pronounce some words.

Ⓒ It tells where to find more information.

Ⓓ It tells the most important words in the passage.

32. What job did pioneer men do?

Ⓐ got meat ready for winter

Ⓑ made candles and soap

Ⓒ gathered eggs and vegetables

Ⓓ cut logs for firewood

33. The author **most likely** wrote "Pioneer Days" to

Ⓐ show what life was like for pioneers.

Ⓑ teach how to live like a pioneer.

Ⓒ get readers to live a simpler life.

Ⓓ tell a funny story about life long ago.

34. Pioneer families had to work a lot. What did pioneer families do for fun?

_____

_____

_____

_____

35. Which sentence is a good summary of "Pioneer Days"?

Ⓐ Pioneer fathers had to feed the animals, clear the land, cut down trees, plow the fields, plant seeds, and cut firewood.

Ⓑ President Lincoln passed a law that let pioneer families have land if they lived and worked on it for five years.

Ⓒ Pioneer parents are like parents today because they hugged and loved their children.

Ⓓ It took lots of hard work by every member of a pioneer family to make the land a good place to live and farm.

Read the recipe. Then answer the questions. For multiple-choice items, darken the circle by the correct answer. For the open-ended item, write the answer.

Applesauce

You will need:

8 large green apples

1 cup water

1 cup sugar

1/2 teaspoon cinnamon

Wash the apples, cut them in quarters, and remove the stems and cores.

Put the cut apples in a large pot and add the water. Cook for about 20 minutes or until the apples are soft.

Put the cooked apples through a strainer. Stir in the sugar and then the cinnamon. Serve warm or cold.

36. How many different ingredients do you need to make applesauce?

Ⓐ two

Ⓑ four

Ⓒ six

Ⓓ eight

37. The recipe is told by

Ⓐ saying how it is different from other recipes.

Ⓑ describing different ways to eat apples.

Ⓒ listing the order of steps to make applesauce.

Ⓓ explaining where applesauce came from.

38. Read this sentence from the recipe.

> Wash the apples, cut them in <u>quarters</u>, and remove the stems and cores.

In this sentence, the word <u>quarters</u> means

Ⓐ four pieces.

Ⓑ 15 minutes.

Ⓒ 25 cents.

Ⓓ a place where a soldier lives.

39. How long should you cook the apples?

Ⓐ 30 minutes

Ⓑ one hour

Ⓒ until they are soft

Ⓓ until they are cut up

© HMH Supplemental Publishers Inc.
© Houghton Mifflin Harcourt Publishing Company

40. What is the core of an apple?

(A) the center

(B) the stem

(C) the skin

(D) the bottom

41. What <u>three</u> things should you do to the apples **before** you start cooking?

_____

_____

_____

_____

Read the passage. Then answer the questions. For multiple-choice items, darken the circle by the correct answer. For the open-ended item, write the answer.

Growing Bean Sprouts

Materials:

- 1 quart jar with a wide mouth
- 1 lid for the jar
- a handful of dry beans
- water and soap

First, wash and dry the jar and lid with soap and water. Ask an adult to poke ten holes in the lid. Wash the beans in water. Put the beans in the jar. Fill the jar with water. Put the lid on the jar. Put the jar of beans in a dark place for one night.

The next day, pour the water out of the jar through the holes. Shake the jar to get out all the water. Turn the jar on its side. This will give the beans room to spread out. Place the jar in a dark place.

Twice a day, rinse the beans. Pour off the water. Place the jar on its side and return it to the dark place. Within two days the seeds should begin sprouting.

42. Why do you poke holes in the jar lid?

   Ⓐ   to keep the beans safe

   Ⓑ   to spread out the beans

   Ⓒ   to pour out water

   Ⓓ   to let the beans fall out

43. How often should the beans be rinsed?

   Ⓐ   twice a day

   Ⓑ   once a week

   Ⓒ   twice a week

   Ⓓ   once a month

44. Which step does the picture show?

   Ⓐ   Poke holes in the lid.

   Ⓑ   Put the jar on its side.

   Ⓒ   Pour the water off the beans.

   Ⓓ   Wash the jar and lid.

45. What is the passage mostly about?

   Ⓐ   what bean sprouts are used for

   Ⓑ   how to grow bean sprouts

   Ⓒ   where to find bean sprouts

   Ⓓ   the history of bean sprouts

46. How is the information in this passage mainly organized?

   Ⓐ   by giving reasons for growing bean sprouts

   Ⓑ   by comparing bean sprouts to other plants

   Ⓒ   by giving steps on how to grow bean sprouts

   Ⓓ   by lisiting problems with bean sprouts and the solutions

47. You would **most likely** find bean sprouts growing

    (A) in deep soil.

    (B) in a dark, damp place.

    (C) in a sunny, dry place.

    (D) in soap and water.

48. What should you gather together **before** you start the project?

_____

_____

_____

_____

Language Arts and Vocabulary Practice Test

Language Arts Practice Test

Read the passage. Then answer the questions. Darken the circle by the correct answer.

(1) I just love a parade. (2) I like to see the marching bands. (3) I like to see the clowns. (4) The loud music always makes me want to clap my hands. (5) I also enjoy the floats. (6) The floats with storybook characters are the best! (7) My favorite was a float with three mouses on it. (8) Them were funny!

1. What is the **best** way to combine sentences 2 and 3?

   Ⓐ I like to see the marching bands, like to see clowns.

   Ⓑ I like to see the marching bands and the clowns.

   Ⓒ I like the marching bands and to see the clowns.

2. What is the correct way to write sentence 7?

   Ⓐ My favorite was a float with three mouse's on it.

   Ⓑ My favorite was a float with three mice on it.

   Ⓒ correct as is

3. Read sentence 8.

Them were funny!

   What is the correct way to write the underlined pronoun?

   Ⓐ Themselves

   Ⓑ Their

   Ⓒ They

Name _____ Date _____

Read the passage. Then answer the questions. Darken the circle by the correct answer.

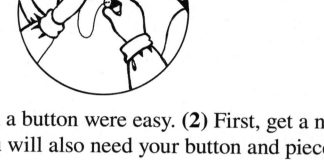

(1) Sewing on a button were easy. (2) First, get a needle and thread. (3) You will also need your button and piece of clothing. (4) Choose a thread color to match the clothing. (5) Next, thread the needle and sew on the button tightly. (6) Then, make a knot in the thread. (7) Last, you the thread.

4. Read sentence 1.

> Sewing on a button <u>were</u> easy.

What is the correct way to write the underlined verb?

Ⓐ be

Ⓑ are

Ⓒ is

5. What is the correct way to write sentence 3?

Ⓐ You will also need our button and piece of clothing.

Ⓑ You will also need its button a piece of clothing.

Ⓒ correct as is

6. What is the correct way to write sentence 7?

Ⓐ Last, you should cut the thread.

Ⓑ Last, the thread.

Ⓒ Last, the thread should cut.

Darken the circle by the correct answer.

7. What describing word **best** completes this sentence?

> Monday was a _____ day.

Ⓐ rainy

Ⓑ shines

Ⓒ sky

8. What word completes the sentence?

> A _____ of geese flew in a V shape.

Ⓐ herd

Ⓑ flock

Ⓒ litter

9. Which verb correctly completes this sentence?

> They _____ under a shady tree.

Ⓐ sitted

Ⓑ sat

Ⓒ have sit

10. Read these sentences.

> Bart likes to sled. Jasmine likes to sled.

What is the **best** way to combine them?

Ⓐ Bart and Jasmine like to sled.

Ⓑ Bart likes to sled and Jasmine likes to sled.

Ⓒ Bart likes to sled, Jasmine likes to sled.

11. Which word can take the place of the underlined words?

> The <u>girl</u> eats a salad.

(A) They

(B) Her

(C) She

12. Which verb correctly completes this sentence?

> Last week, our bird _____ away.

(A) flown

(B) flied

(C) flew

13. Choose the sentence that is correct.

(A) We weren't get wet in the rain.

(B) My brother put those toys in the box.

(C) We don't have no milk left.

14. Choose the sentence that is in correct word order.

(A) Don bought flowers for his mother.

(B) Flowers for his mother Don bought.

(C) Bought flowers did Don for his mother.

Name _____ Date _____

Read Cammy's report. Then answer the questions. Darken the circle by the correct answer.

(1) Do you know what earth day is? (2) This holiday was first held on April 22 1970. (3) It began in the United States. (4) People wanted to show they were worried about our air and water. (5) Since then, the day has become a party for Earth. (6) Now people around the world get together (7) They do things to keep Earth cleen.

15. What is the correct way to write sentence 1?

Ⓐ Do you know what earth Day is?

Ⓑ Do you know what Earth Day is?

Ⓒ Do you know What Earth day is?

16. What is the correct way to write sentence 2?

Ⓐ This holiday was first held on April 22, 1970.

Ⓑ This holiday was first held on April, 22 1970.

Ⓒ This holiday was first held on April, 22, 1970.

17. Which punctuation mark belongs at the end of sentence 6?

Ⓐ .

Ⓑ ?

Ⓒ ,

18. Which word is misspelled in sentence 7?

They do <u>things</u> to <u>keep</u> Earth <u>cleen</u>.

Ⓐ things

Ⓑ keep

Ⓒ cleen

Name _____ Date _____

Read Yoko's story. Then answer the questions. Darken the circle by the correct answer.

(1) I couldn't find my cat blacky. (2) Then I saw my neighbor, Mrs. Brown, looking up in our tree. (3) Blacky was stuck high up in the tree! (4) Mrs. Brown got a ladder and climbed up close to Blacky. (5) Blackys fur stood up on end! (6) "Blacky is afraid, said Mrs. Brown." (7) Mrs. Brown moved slowly and talked softly. (8) Blacky walked over to Mrs. Brown. (9) She saved my cat!

19. What is the correct way to write sentence 1?

   Ⓐ I couldn't find my Cat blacky.

   Ⓑ I couldn't find my cat Blacky.

   Ⓒ correct as is

20. What is the correct way to write sentence 5?

   Ⓐ Black'ys fur stood up on end!

   Ⓑ Blackies fur stood up on end!

   Ⓒ Blacky's fur stood up on end!

21. What is the correct way to write sentence 6?

   Ⓐ "Blacky" is afraid, said Mrs. Brown.

   Ⓑ "Blacky is afraid," said Mrs. Brown.

   Ⓒ "Blacky is afraid, said "Mrs. Brown."

Darken the circle by the correct answer.

22. Which correctly spelled word fits the sentence?

> The cup has a broken _____ .

Ⓐ handle

Ⓑ handul

Ⓒ handel

23. Mark the sentence that has the correct capitalization and punctuation.

Ⓐ June 6 is the last day of school.

Ⓑ How is your grandmother feeling.

Ⓒ Tucson arizona is an interesting city.

24. What is the correct greeting for a letter?

Ⓐ Dear Grandma

Ⓑ Dear, Grandma

Ⓒ Dear Grandma,

25. Choose the sentence that is correct.

Ⓐ I just finished reading Marys new book <u>Five Fuzzy Bugs</u>.

Ⓑ I just finished reading Mary's new book <u>Five Fuzzy Bugs</u>.

Ⓒ I just finished reading Marys' new book <u>Five Fuzzy Bugs</u>.

26. Mark the sentence that has a punctuation error.

Ⓐ Why are you late?

Ⓑ Im tired today.

Ⓒ I need some sleep.

27. Which word in this sentence needs a capital letter?

My friend lives in atlanta, Georgia.

Ⓐ friend

Ⓑ lives

Ⓒ atlanta

28. Which correctly spelled word fits the sentence?

How much _____ do you need to buy a new soccer ball?

Ⓐ money

Ⓑ mony

Ⓒ munny

29. Mark the sentence that has correct punctuation and capitalization.

Ⓐ Have you ever been to Orlando, Florida?

Ⓑ Thats where Disney World is

Ⓒ We're going in july.

Name _____   Date _____

Read the passage. Then answer the questions. Darken the circle by the correct answer.

The White House

The White House is where the President of the United States lives. The White House was built over two hundred years ago. It is almost as old as the country.

George Washington was the first President of the United States. He chose the place where the White House would be built. But he never lived in the White House. It was not finished in time.

The house was completed later when John Adams was President. John Adams was the first President to live in the White House.

Today the White House proudly stands for the United States of America.

30. What word in the passage means the **opposite** of last?

Ⓐ two

Ⓑ over

Ⓒ first

Ⓓ old

31. Read this sentence from the passage.

> It is almost as old as the country.

Which meaning of country is used in this sentence?

Ⓐ an area outside of a city

Ⓑ a place that has its own government

Ⓒ a kind of music

Ⓓ a place where people farm

32. Read these sentences from the passage.

> It was not finished in time. The house was completed later when John Adams was President.

What clue word helps the reader know what completed means?

Ⓐ finished

Ⓑ time

Ⓒ later

Ⓓ when

33. Read this sentence from the passage.

> Today the White House proudly stands for the United States of America.

What does the word proudly mean?

Ⓐ not proud

Ⓑ one who is proud

Ⓒ in a proud way

Ⓓ very proud

Name _____ **Date** _____

Darken the circle by the correct answer.

34. Read the sentence.

> I can walk the dog if I stay on the sidewalk.

What does the word sidewalk mean?

(A) a wooden walkway on a beach

(B) a part of a street where bikes can go

(C) a sign found on the side of a building

(D) a place to walk on the side of a road

35. Which word has the **same** root word as discover?

(A) over

(B) covered

(C) disc

(D) cove

36. Which definition of wing is used in the sentence below?

> **wing (wing)**
>
> *noun*
> 1. part of a bird's body
>
> *noun*
> 2. part of an airplane
>
> *noun*
> 3. part of a building
>
> *verb*
> 4. to fly

> The baby robin has a broken wing.

(A) definition 1

(B) definition 2

(C) definition 3

(D) definition 4

© HMH Supplemental Publishers Inc.
© Houghton Mifflin Harcourt Publishing Company

37. Read the sentence.

> We heard a strange <u>noise</u> coming from the house.

What word means the **same** or **almost the same** as <u>noise</u>?

(A) sound

(B) window

(C) smile

(D) story

38. Mark the word with a meaning that fits both sentences.

> We are learning how to put words in A, B, C _____.
>
> I will phone in an _____ for a pizza.

(A) buy

(B) read

(C) order

(D) eat

39. Choose the word that **best** completes the sentence.

> I was _____ and didn't hear the phone ring.

(A) awake

(B) tired

(C) sleepy

(D) asleep

40. Read the sentence.

> I was on <u>pins and needles</u> waiting for my brother to arrive at the airport.

What does <u>pins and needles</u> mean?

(A) sad

(B) excited

(C) sleepy

(D) in pain

Writing
Practice Test

Writing Prompt 1: Opinion

Plan your writing. Write your response on a separate sheet of paper. Then proofread what you have written.

What is your favorite thing to do on the playground? Why is this your favorite thing to do? Explain to a family member why you like to do it.

As you write your response, be sure to

- Write about only one thing.
- Include at least two reasons you like it.
- Give details that support your reasons.
- Include an introduction, a middle, and an ending.
- Write in complete sentences.

Writing Prompt 2: Informative

Plan your writing. Write your response on a separate sheet of paper. Then proofread what you have written.

Think about a special place in your community. Tell what makes this place special. Describe it to a person who has never been there.

As you write your response, be sure to

- Write about only one place.
- Give details that make your writing clear. Be sure to describe what the place looks like.
- Write in complete sentences.

Writing Prompt 3: Narrative

Plan your writing. Write your response on a separate sheet of paper. Then proofread what you have written.

> Write a story about two friends who work together to solve a problem. Write the story for a friend to read aloud.

As you write your response, be sure to

- Describe where the story takes place.
- Describe the characters in the story.
- Tell your story events in order.
- Tell what the problem is and how it is solved.

Answers

Tips and Practice Section

Reading Practice: Literature

1. C

2. B

3. D

4. A

5. A

6. B

7. Juan won a third-place medal.

8. D

9. C

10. C

11. B

12. D

13. A

14. clean the light

15. D

16. B

17. B

18. A

19. C

20. D

21. B

22. a field of trees in winter

Reading Practice: Informational Text

1. C

2. C

3. A

4. D

5. B

6. B

7. 2, 3, 1, 4

8. A

9. C

10. D

11. B

12. A

13. B

14. to look for a yellow spot that shows I like butter

15. B

16. C

17. A

18. B

19. D

20. C

21. Spread peanut butter on pinecone.

22. C

23. C

24. D

25. B

26. B

27. A

28. You will need

Language Arts Practice

1. C

2. A

3. B

4. C

5. C

6. A

7. B

8. C

9. B

10. B

11. A

12. C

13. A

14. C

15. B

© HMH Supplemental Publishers Inc.

© Houghton Mifflin Harcourt Publishing Company

16. C

17. C

18. A

19. B

20. C

21. B

22. C

23. B

24. A

25. A

26. B

27. C

28. A

29. B

30. B

31. B

32. B

33. A

34. A

35. C

36. B

37. B

38. A

Vocabulary Practice

1. D

2. B

3. A

4. C

5. D

6. B

7. B

8. A

9. B

10. C

11. D

12. A

13. D

14. C

15. B

16. D

17. A

18. B

Writing Practice

See Scoring Rubric on page 137.

Prompt 1: Students should write an essay to a friend about their favorite book. Students should include at least two reasons and supporting details explaining why they like the book.

Prompt 2: Students should write instructions for a new game they've invented. Students should name the game and include directions in order.

Prompt 3: Students should write a story about a family with a child their age that moves to their neighborhood. The story should include details about where the story takes place and about the characters.

© HMH Supplemental Publishers Inc.
© Houghton Mifflin Harcourt Publishing Company

Practice Test

Reading Practice Test

1. A

2. C

3. B

4. C

5. D

6. A

7. Alice writes Wanda a letter. Alice asks Wanda to come visit.

8. B

9. A

10. D

11. B

12. C

13. A

14. Lonzell–work a puppet; Malcolm–read the lines

15. A

16. B

17. D

18. C

19. B

20. C

21. The picture shows a cat on a couch in a living room.

22. C

23. D

24. B

25. A

26. C

27. A

28. 3, 2, 1, 4

29. C

30. B

31. A

32. D

33. A

34. They told stories and played games after supper.

35. D

36. B

37. C

38. A

39. C

40. A

41. Wash them. Cut them in quarters. Remove the stems and cores.

42. C

43. A

44. D

45. B

46. C

47. B

48. quart jar with wide mouth, lid, dry beans, soap

Language Arts Practice Test

1. B

2. B

3. C

4. C

5. C

6. A

7. A

8. B

9. B

10. A

11. C

12. C

13. B

14. A

15. B

16. A

17. A

18. C

19. B

20. C

21. B

22. A

23. A

24. C

25. B

26. B

27. C

28. A

29. A

Vocabulary Practice Test

30. C

31. B

32. A

33. C

34. D

35. B

36. A

37. A

38. C

39. D

40. B

Writing Practice Test
See Scoring Rubric on page 137.

Prompt 1: Students should write an essay to a family member about their favorite thing to do on a playground. Students should include at least two reasons and supporting details explaining why they like the activity.

Prompt 2: Students should describe a special place to a person who has never been there. Students should include descriptive details that describe how the place looks.

Prompt 3: Students should write a story about two friends who work together to solve a problem. The story should include details about where the story takes place and about the characters. The story should also identify the problem and provide a solution.

4-Point Rubric For Writing Prompts

Use the following rubric to score your students' response to the writing prompts.

A *4-point* response demonstrates **advanced** success with the writing task. The essay:

- focuses consistently on the topic
- shows effective organization throughout, with smooth transitions
- offers thoughtful ideas
- develops ideas thoroughly, using examples and details
- shows good control of written language

A *3-point* response demonstrates **competent** success with the writing task. In general, the essay:

- focuses mostly on the topic
- shows effective organization, with minor lapses
- offers mostly thoughtful ideas
- develops ideas adequately and uses some general and some specific reasons and evidence
- shows general control of written language

A *2-point* response demonstrates **limited** success with the writing task. In general, the essay:

- includes some ideas that are related to the topic but does not focus consistently on the topic
- shows some organization, with noticeable gaps in the logical flow of ideas
- offers predictable ideas
- develops or supports ideas with little elaboration and reasoning
- shows limited control of written language

A *1-point* response demonstrates **emerging** effort with the writing task. In general, the essay:

- shows little awareness of the topic
- lacks organization
- offers confusing ideas
- develops ideas in a minimal way, if at all, or gives only a few reasons
- shows major problems with control of written language